DICTIONARY

OF MODERN

ACRONYMS &
ABBREVIATIONS

$4.95

Cat. No. DAG-1

DICTIONARY

OF MODERN

ACRONYMS &

ABBREVIATIONS

by Milton Goldstein

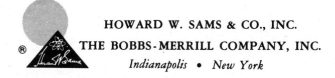

HOWARD W. SAMS & CO., INC.

THE BOBBS-MERRILL COMPANY, INC.

Indianapolis • *New York*

FIRST EDITION

FIRST PRINTING — JULY, 1963

DICTIONARY OF MODERN ACRONYMS
& ABBREVIATIONS

Library of Congress Catalog Card Number: 63-17022

FOREWORD

Acronyms and abbreviations are constantly becoming a greater part of our everyday lives. Many, such as RADAR and NASA, are in common use, even by the general public. However, there are many which are known only to the personnel engaged in a specific vocation. The author has long believed that a single source for the meanings of all acronyms and abbreviations was needed. Consequently, he started a card file, mainly for his own use. As each new term was encountered, a new card was made and added. This book is the result of an accumulation of cards over a period of some three years.

Before a book of this nature can gain wide acceptance and usage, it must be easy to use. Every effort has been made to make this book as easy to use as is humanly possible. All terms are listed in bold-face type. Catchwords at the top of each page show the beginning and ending words of the two facing pages. All terms are listed in a strict alphabetical order without regard to separations or punctuation. Thus, there can be no doubt where a term should be—it can only fit in one place. Many times, a term has more than one meaning; all are listed under a single entry separated by periods. Thus, valuable time, which would be wasted hunting through separate entries for each meaning, is saved.

Many times, especially for foreign or lesser-known terms, additional information is included within parentheses to clarify the meaning. For example, most U.S. readers may not be familiar with the letters "DOT." They still have little meanings when we say the letters stand for "Department of Transport." However, included in the parentheses is the fact that this is a "Canadian agency that issues radio licenses—similar to the FCC." Now the meaning becomes apparent.

This book is as up-to-date and complete as is possible to make it, however, in any work of this magnitude some terms will no doubt have been omitted. Also, new terms are being "coined" daily. It is our intention to periodically issue revised editions of this dictionary; thus, your suggestions for new terms and meanings will be welcomed.

June, 1963

A

A—Accelerating contactor or relay (JIC and NMTBA term). Advance (resistance alloy). Aircraft (Air Force designation). Aircraft carrier. Air - launched (Dept. of Defense missile designation). Ampere. Analog Analyzer. Asbestos wire. Structural part.

AA—Administrative assistant. Aviatsionnaya Armiya (Russian Air Army). Felted asbestos, asbestos braid cable.

A-A—Air-to-air.

AAA—Antiaircraft artillery.

AAAA—Army Aviation Association of America.

AAAE—American Association of Airport Executives.

AAAIS—Advanced army airborne indicating system (cockpit display system developed by Douglas Aircraft Co.) Antiaircraft Artillery Information Service.

AAAR—Association for the Advancement of Aeronautical Research (France).

AAAS—American Academy of Arts and Sciences.

AAB—Aircraft Accident Board (U. S. military term). Antiaircraft balloon.

AABM—American Association of Battery Manufacturers.

AAC—Aeronautical Advisory Council. Aeronautical approach chart. Alaskan Air Command. Antiaircraft common (U. S. Navy).

AACB—Aeronautics and Astronautics Coordinating Board.

AACC—American Automatic Control Council.

AACE—American Association of Cost Engineers.

AACP—Air carrier contract personnel.

AACS—Airways and Air Communications Service.

AACSM—Airways and Air Communications Service Manual.

AADA—Advanced air depot area (U. S. Air Force). Antiaircraft-defended area.

AADC—Antiair Director Center.

AADCP—Army air defense command post.

AAE—American Association of Engineers (8 S. Michigan Ave., Chicago 3, Ill.). Army Aviation Engineers.

AAFB—Andrews Air Force Base.

AAFCE—Allied Air Force, Central Europe.

AAFCWF—Army and Air Force Central Welfare Fund.

AAFEMPS—Army and Air Force Exchange and Motion Picture Service.

AAFES—Army and Air Force Exchange Service.

AAFNE—Allied Air Force, Northern Europe.

AAFPS—Army and Air Force Postal Service.

AAFSE—Allied Air Force, Southern Europe.

AAFWB—Army and Air Force Wage Board.

AAG—Air Adjutant General (U. S. Air Force).

AAGR—Air-to-air gunnery range (U. S. Air Force).

AAHA—Awaiting action of higher authority (U. S. Armed Forces term).

AAI—Air - to - air identification. American Audio Institute. Angle-of-attack indicator.

AAIC—Allied Air Intelligence Center.

AAJCS—Anglo - American Joint Chiefs of Staff.

AAKM—Association for the Advancement of the Knowledge of Materials. (Netherlands organization).

AAM—Air-to-air missile.

AAMG—Antiaircraft machine gun.

AAMI—American Association of Machinery Importers.

AAOC—Antiaircraft Operations Center.

AAP—Aerodynamics Advisory Panel (Atomic Energy Commission).

AAPD—American Academy of Professional Draftsmen.

AAPIU—Allied Aerial Photographic Interpretation Unit.

AAPMA—Automotive and Aviation Parts Manufacturing Association.

AAQM—Acting Assistant Quartermaster (U. S. Marine Corps).

AAR—Aircraft Accident Record. Association of American Railroads.

AARS—Army Aircraft Repair Ship.

AAS—Advanced antenna system. American Astronautical Society.

AASE—Association for Applied Solar Energy.

AASR—Airport and airways surveillance radar.

AATC—Antiaircraft Training Center (U. S. Navy).

AAT&TC—Antiaircraft Training Test Center (U. S. Navy).

AAUP—American Association of University Professors (1785 Massachusetts Ave. N.W., Washington 6, D.C.).

AAV—Airborne assault vehicle.

AAVSO—American Association of Variable Star Observers.

AB—Able - bodied seaman (U. S. Navy). Aeronautical Board (U. S. Air Force). Air base. Antenna supports (JAN nomenclature).

Aviation Boatswain's Mate (U. S. Navy).

ABA—American Bankers' Association.

ABATU—Advance Base Air Task Unit. Advanced Base Aviation Training Unit (U. S. Navy).

ABB—Automatic back bias.

ABC—Advanced biomedical capsule (Lockheed space vehicle for chimpanzees). Allocations for budgetary control (Rocketdyne budget-control system). American-British-Canadian. Atlantic base command. Atomic, biological, chemical. Automatic bandwidth control. Automatic bass compensation. Automatic bias control. Automatic boiling-column reactor. Automatic brightness control.

ABCD—ACF building-block communications devices. Advanced base construction depot (U. S. Navy).

ABCCTC—Advanced Base Combat Communication Training Center (U. S. Navy).

ABD—Advanced base depot. Advanced base dock (U. S. Navy).

ABDACOM—Advanced base depot area command (U. S. Navy).

ABDL—Automatic binary data link (an air-to-ground link developed by Stromberg-Carlson).

ABES—Aerospace business environment simulator (developed by Lockheed).

ABF—Aircraft Battle Force (U. S. Navy).

ABG—Air Base Group (U. S. Navy).

ABGP—Air Base Group (U. S. Air Force).

ABLE—Autonetics base-line equipment (gyroscope direction finder). Azimuth-reference base line.

ABM—Automated batch mixing.

ABMA—Army Ballistic Missile Agency.

ABMC—Army Ballistic Missile Committee.

ABMEWS—Anti - ballistic - missile early warning system.

ABN—Airborne.

ABNINF—Airborne infantry.

ABO—Astable blocking oscillator.

ABPA—Advanced Base Personnel Administration (U. S. Navy).

ABPG—Advanced base proving ground (U. S. Navy).

ABPO—Advanced base personnel officer (U. S. Navy).

ABPU—Advanced base personnel unit (U. S. Navy).

ABR—Amphibian boat reconnaissance aircraft (U. S. Navy).

ABRB—Advanced base receiving barracks (U. S. Navy).

ABRD—Advanced base repair depot (U. S. Navy). Advanced base reshipment depot (U. S. Navy).

ABRES—Advanced ballistic re-entry system.

ABRL—Army Ballistic Research Laboratory.

ABS—Acrylonitrile - butadiene - styrene (insulation material). Air base simulator. Air base squadron (U. S. Air Force).

ABSAP—Airborne search and attack plotter (U. S. Navy).

ABSD—Advanced base sectional dock (U. S. Navy). Advanced base supply depot (U. S. Navy).

ABT—About.

ABTF—Airborne task force.

ABTU—Advanced base torpedo unit (U. S. Navy). Advanced base training unit (U. S. Navy). Air bombers training unit (U. S. Navy).

ABWG—Air base wing (U. S. Air Force).

AC—Admiral commanding (U. S. Navy). Accept (telephone term). Accumulator. Air command. Air controlman (U. S. Navy).

Aircraft. Airdrome control. Alaskan Command. Ambulance Corps. Amphibious Corps. Antarctic continent. Armored cable.

ACA—American Communications Association (5 Beekman St., New York, N.Y.). American Cryptogram Association. American Crystallographic Association. Asbestos aircraft wire. Associative content addressable memory. Automatic circuit analyzer.

AC-AL—Acid alum.

ACAN—Army command and administrative network.

ACAS—Assistant chief of air staff.

ACAV—Automatic circuit analyzer and verifier.

ACBB—American Council for Better Broadcasts (423 N. Pinckney St., Madison 3, Wis.).

ACC—Accumulator. Air control center. Air coordinating committee. Allied Control Commission. Area control center. Astronomical great circle course. Automatic color control.

ACCCE—Association of Consulting Chemists and Chemical Engineers.

ACCESS—Aircraft communication and electronic signaling (developed by Motorola and General Precision).

ACC/NAV—Air Traffic Control and Navigation Panel of the Air Coordinating Committee.

ACCW—Alternating-current continuous wave.

ACDA—Arms Control and Disarmament Agency (U.S. government).

ACDC—Army Combat Developments Command.

ACDR—Aero commander.

ACE—Aerospace control environment (U.S. Air Force program). Automatic circuit exchange. Automatic computing engine (built by National Physical Lab., **[Cont.]**

England). Automatic continuity equipment. Automatic continuous evaporation.

ACEC—Association of Consulting Engineers of Canada.

ACERP—Advanced communications electronics requirements plan.

ACES—Automatic controls evaluation simulator (developed by Chance Vought, Astronautics Div.).

ACEW—Association of Communications Workers.

ACGF—Automatic continuous function generation.

ACGMR—Ad Hoc Committee for Guided Missile Reliability.

ACI—Air combat information. Alloy Casting Institute (1001 Franklin Ave., Garden City, N.Y.). Altitude command indicator.

ACIC—Aeronautical chart and information center.

ACIL—American Council of Independent Laboratories, Inc.

ACK—Acknowledge.

ACL—Automatic carrier landing system. Armored cable, lead sheath.

ACLD—Above clouds (CAA term).

ACLS—Automatic carrier landing system.

ACM—Active countermeasures. Association of Canadian Manufacturers. Association for Computing Machinery. Axon cylinder membrane.

ACMA—Alumina Ceramics Manufacturers' Association.

ACME—Association of Consulting Management Engineers.

ACMS—Army command management system.

ACN—Automatic celestial navigation.

ACNO—Assistant Chief of Naval Operations.

ACO—Administrative contracting officer.

ACOE—Automatic checkout equipment.

ACORN—Automatic checkout and recording equipment (developed by De Havilland Aircraft, Ltd.).

ACP—Allied communication publications. Auxiliary check point. Azimuth change pulses.

ACR—Abandon call and retry (telephone term).

ACRA—Audio Components Representatives' Association.

ACRE—Automatic checkout and readiness equipment.

ACRS—Advisory committee on reactor safeguards.

ACS—Accumulator switches. Alaska communications system (also known as "White Alice"). American Chemical Society. Armament control system. Assistant chief of staff. Audio conducted susceptibility. Automatic control system.

ACSC—Army Command and Staff College.

ACSM—American Congress on Surveying and Mapping.

ACSR—Aluminum conductor, steel-reinforced (cable).

ACSS—Analog computer subsystem.

ACT—Acetate cloth tape. Air Cavalry Troop. Air control team. Armored cable.

ACTER—Active filter.

ACTP—Air cavalry troop (provisional).

ACTS—Arc current time simulator (manufactured by Multi-Amp Electronic Corp.).

ACU—Acceleration compensation unit. Automatic calling unit (telephone term).

ACV—Air-cushion vehicles. Armored cable (exposed locations).

ACW—Aircraft control and warning.

ACWO—Aircraft control and warn-

10

ing officer.

AD—Active duty. Actuator drive. Air defense. Air division. Alloy diffused. Attention display. Automatic detection. Aviation machinist's mate (U.S. Navy). Destroyer tender (U.S. Navy).

ADA—Aerojet differential analyzer. Air defense artillery. Angular differentiating-integrating accelerometer. Automatic data acquisition.

ADACC—Automatic data acquisition and computer complex.

ADAD—Air defense artillery director.

ADALINE—Adaptive linear classification machine.

ADAO—Air defense artillery officer.

ADAPS—Automatic display and plotting system.

ADAPSO—Association of Data Processing Service Organizations.

ADAT—Automatic data accumulator and transfer.

ADC—Aide-de-camp. Air-data computer. Air defense command. Analog-to-digital converter. Automatic drive control.

ADCAD—Airways data collecting and distribution.

ADCC—Air defense control center.

ADC COMNET—Air defense command communications network.

ADCI—American Die Casting Institute.

ADCOM—Air defense command network.

ADCS—Air defense coordination system.

ADD—Aerospace digital development (UNIVAC airborne computer).

ADDAR—Automatic digital data acquisition and recording (developed by Monitor Systems, Inc.).

ADDC—Air defense direction center.

ADDRESOR—Analog - to - digital data-reduction system for oceanographic research.

ADEPT—Automatic data extractor and plotting table. Automatic dynamic evaluation by programmed testing (developed by Ortronix, Inc., Orlando, Fla.).

ADES—Air defense engineering service.

ADF—Air Defense Force. Automatic direction finder.

ADFAP—Automatic direction finder approach.

ADI—Air defense intercept. American Documentation Institute (1728 N. St. N.W., Washington 6, D.C.).

ADIL—Air defense identification line.

ADIOS—Automatic digital input-output system.

ADIS—Automatic data interchange system (developed for FAA by Teletype Corp.).

ADIT—Analog-digital integrating translator (developed by Weston, Newark, N.J.).

ADIZ—Air defense identification zone.

ADL—Acceptable defect level.

ADLO—Air defense liaison officer.

ADMA—Aviation Distributors and Manufacturers' Association.

ADN—Accession designation number.

ADO—Advanced development objective (U.S. Air Force). Audio decade oscillator.

ADONIS—Automatic digital on-line instrumentation system (developed by Blackburn Electronics Ltd., England).

ADP—Ammonium dihydrogen phosphate (piezoelectric crystal used in sonar). Apparatus drawings project. Automatic data processing.

ADPC—Automatic data processing center.

ADPS—Automatic data processing system.

ADPT—Adapter.

ADR—Adder. Analog-to-digital recorder.

ADRAC—Automatic digital recording and control.

ADRES—Army data retrieval engineering system.

ADRM—Airdrome.

ADRS—Address.

ADRT—Analog data recorder transcriber (Honeywell data-handling system).

ADS—Air defense sector. Air defense system.

ADSEC—Air Defense Systems Engineering Committee.

ADSID—Air Defense Survey of Intelligence Division. Air Defense Systems Integration Division (U.S. Air Force).

ADSMO—Air defense systems management office (U.S. Air Force).

ADSP—Automatic dispatching stick repeater.

ADU—Accumulation and distribution unit. Angular display unit.

ADV—Arc-drop voltage.

ADW—Air defense warning.

ADX—Automatic data exchange.

AE—Ammunition ship (U.S. Navy).

A-E—Architect-Engineer.

AEA—Atomic energy act. Atomic Energy Authority (British governmental agency).

AEBA—Automatic emergency broadcast alerting.

AEC—Atomic Energy Commission.

AED—Association of Electronic Distributors.

AEDC—Arnold Engineering Development Center (U.S. Air Force, Rocket Engine Test Center, Tullahoma, Tenn.).

AEE—Absolute essential equipment.

Atomic energy establishment (British agency).

AEEC—Airlines Electronic Engineering Committee.

AEETF—Army's Electronic Environmental Test Facility (to be built in Arizona).

AEG—Active-element group.

AEGIS—Astro electronic gimballess inertial system (developed by Martin Co.).

AEI—Azimuth error indicator.

AEIC—Association of Edison Illuminating Companies.

AEM—Aeronautical mobile.

AEMT—Automatically erectable modular torus (space station configuration).

AEP—American Electric Power (an integrated, interconnected electric power network of six operating companies in parts of seven states).

AEPEM—Association of Electronic Parts and Equipment Manufacturers.

AEPG—Army Electronic Proving Ground (Ft. Huachuca, Ariz.).

AEPS—American Electroplaters' Society.

AER—Aeronautics.

AERIS—Airborne electronic ranging instrumentation system (developed by Cubic Corp.).

AERNL—Aeronautical.

AES—Aerospace Electrical Society. Aircraft Electrical Society. American Electroplaters' Society. Audio Engineering Society.

AET—Approximate exposure time.

AEV—Aerothermodynamic/elastic.

AEW—Airborne early warning. Aircraft early warning.

AEWA—Airborne early warning aircraft.

AEW&C—Airborne early warning and control.

AEW&CON—Airborne early warning and control.

AEWPC—Army Electronic Warfare Policy Committee (Signal Corps).

AF—Admiral of the Fleet. Aeronautical fixed. Air Force. Alternating flow. Asbestos-covered, heat-resistant fixture wire. Audio frequency. Provision storeship (U.S. Navy).

AFA—Air Force Association (Mills Building, Washington 6, D.C.).

AFAC—Air Force Armament Center. Automatic field analog computer.

AFAFC—Air Force accounting and finance center.

AFA-SEF—Air Force Association—Space Education Foundation.

AFAUX—Air Force auxiliary field.

AFB—Air Force base.

AFBMC—Air Force ballistic missile committee.

AFBMD—Air Force ballistic missile division.

AFBMDFO—Air Force ballistic missile division field office.

AFBMP—Air Force ballistic missile program.

AFC—Asbestos-covered, heat-resistant cord. Automatic flight control. Automatic frequency control.

AFCAL—Association Francaise De Calcul (French Computing Association).

AFCALTI—French Association for Computation and Data Processing.

AFCCE—Association of Federal Communications Consulting Engineers (710 14th St. N.W., Washington 5, D.C.).

AFCCDD—Air Force Command and Control Development Division.

AFCCE—Association of Federal Communications Consulting Engineers.

AFCE—Automatic flight-control equipment.

AFCEA—Armed Forces Communications and Electronics Association.

AFCMO—Air Force Contract Management Office.

AFCRC—Air Force Cambridge Research Center.

AFCRL—Air Force Cambridge Research Laboratories.

AFCS—Air Force Communications System. Automatic flight-control system.

AFCSA—Air Force Scientific Advisory Board.

AFD—Air Force depot. Automatic fast demagnetization.

AFDAT—Air Force Directorate of Advanced Technology.

AFFTC—Air Force Flight Test Center (Edwards, Calif.).

AFG—Analog function generator.

AFGWRP—Air Force Global Weather Reconnaissance Program.

AFI—Air Filter Institute.

AFIPS—American Federation of Information-Processing Societies.

AFIR—Air Force installation representative.

AFJKT—Air Force job knowledge test.

AFL—Antisymmetric filter.

AFLC—Air Force Logistics Command.

AFLCSO—Air Force Logistics Command Support Office.

AFLD—Airfield.

AFMDC—Air Force Missile Development Center (Holloman Air Force Base, N. Mex.).

AFMTC—Air Force Missile Test Center.

AFNETR—Air Force nuclear engineering test reactor.

AFNOR—French Standards Association.

AFOQT—Air Force Officer Qualification Test.

AFOS—Air Force objective series.

AFOSR—Air Force Office **[Cont.]**

of Scientific Research.

AFPC—Air Force Procurement Circular.

AFPD—Asbestos-covered, heat-resistant cord.

AFPI—Air Force Procurement Instruction.

AFPO—Asbestos-covered, heat-resistant cord.

AFPR—Air Force plant representative.

AFR—Acceptable failure rate. Air Force regulation.

AFRA—French Association of Automatic Control.

AFRD—Air Force Research Division.

AFROTC—Air Force Reserve Officers Training Corps.

AFRS—Armed Forces Radio Service.

AFS—American Field Service. American Foundrymen's Society. Automatic frequency stabilization.

AFSAM—Air Force School of Aviation Medicine (Brooks Air Force Base, Texas).

AFSC—Air Force specialty code. Air Force Staff College. Air Force Systems Command. Armed Forces Staff College.

AFSCC—Air Force Special Communications Center.

AFSJ—Rubber-jacketed, heat-resistant cord.

AFSR—Argonne Fast Source Reactor.

AFSS—Air Force Security Service.

AFSSC—Armed Forces Supply Support Center (Washington, D.C.).

AFSWC—Air Force Special Weapons Center (Kirtland Air Force Base, N. Mex.).

AFSWP—Armed Forces special weapons project.

AFT—Acetate, film tape. Automatic fine tuning.

AFTAC—Air Force Technical Applications Center.

AFTN—Aeronautical fixed telecommunications network.

AFTO—Air Force technical order.

AFTRA—American Federation of TV and Radio Artists (15 W. 44th St., New York 36, N.Y.).

AFUS—Air Force of the United States.

AFWESPAC—Army Forces Western Pacific.

AG—Adjutant General. Aktiengesellschaft. And gate. Miscellaneous auxiliary ship (U.S. Navy).

A/G—Air-to-ground.

AGA—American Gas Association. As good as.

AGA-CS—Air-ground-air communications system.

AGACS—Automatic ground - to - air communications system.

AGARD—Advisory group for aeronautical research and development (NATO Group).

AGAVE—Automatic gimballed-antenna vectoring equipment (automatic tracking antenna system developed by the Cubic Corp.).

AGB—Accessory gear box.

AGC—Amphibious force flagship (U.S. Navy). Associated General Contractors. Automatic gage control. Automatic gain control.

AGCA—Automatic ground control approach.

AGC-GM—Automatic gage control-gagemeter system.

AGCT—Army general classification test.

AGD—Adjutant General's Department.

AGE—Aerospace ground equipment.

AGEP—Advisory group on electronic parts (agency of Dept. of Defense).

AGET—Advisory Group on Electron Tubes (346 Broadway, New York 13, N.Y.).

AGF—Army ground force.

AGFRD—Army Ground Forces Replacement Depot.

A/G GR—Air-to-Ground Gunnery Range.

AGILE—Autonetics General Information Learning Equipment.

AGL—Above ground level. Airborne gun laying radar. Lighthouse tender (U.S. Coast Guard).

AGLC—Air-ground liaison code.

AGM—Missile range instrumentation ship.

AGMEPS—Advisory Group on Management of Electronic Parts Specifications.

AGN—Again.

AGO—Adjutant General's office.

AGOR—Oceanographic research ship.

AGOS—Air-ground operations system.

AGP—Motor torpedo boat tender (U.S. Navy).

AGR—Advanced gas-cooled reactor.

AGREE—Advisory group on reliability of electronic equipment.

AGS—Advanced guidance system (designed by Space Technology Labs., Inc.). American Geographic Society. Hydrographic survey ship (U.S. Navy).

AGU—American Geophysical Union.

AGWAC—Australian guided weapons analog computer (Elliott Bros.).

AH—Ampere-hour. Hospital ship (U. S. Navy).

AHC—Army Hospital Corps.

AHDG—American high-density graphite.

AHP—Air horsepower.

AHR—Aqueous homogeneous reactor.

AHS—American Helicopter Society (2 E. 64th St., New York 21, N.Y.).

AHSR—Air height surveillance radar.

AI—Airborne intercept radar. Aircraft interception. Amplifier input. Azimuth indicator. Impregnated asbestos wire (low-temp).

AIA—Aerospace Industries Association. American Institute of Architects. Argentine Interplanetary Association. Impregnated asbestos wire (low temp, open wiring).

AIAA—American Institute of Aeronautics and Astronautics.

AIBS—American Institute of Biological Sciences.

AIC—Air interception control.

AICA—International Association for Analog Computation.

AICBM—Anti-intercontinental ballistic missile.

AICE—American Institute of Consulting Engineers.

AICHE—American Institute of Chemical Engineers.

AICME—Association Internationale des Constructeurs de Materiel Aerospatial.

AIEE—American Institute of Electrical Engineers.

AID—Airline interline development (developed by Remington Rand). Avalanche injection diode.

AIDA—Automatic instrumented diving assembly.

AIDE—Adapted identification decision equipment.

AIEC—All - Industry Electronics Conference.

AIF—Atomic Industrial Forum.

AIG—Address-indicating group.

AIHA—American Industrial Hygiene Association.

AIIE—American Institute of Industrial Engineers.

15

AILAS—Automatic instrument landing approach system. Automatic instrument low-approach system.

AIM—Add, initial, multiprecision. Acitve inert missile. Alarm-indicating monitor.

AIMACO—Air materiel command automatic compiler (developed by Remington Rand).

AIMC—American Institute of Medical Climatology.

AIME—American Institute of Mining, Metallurgical, and Petroleum Engineers.

AIMO—Audibly instructed manufacturing operations (developed by Westinghouse and Dictaphone Corps.).

AIP—American Institute of Physics (335 E. 45th St., New York 22, N.Y.).

AIPA—American Ionospheric Propagation Association.

AIPE—American Institute of Plant Engineers.

AIRA—Air Force attache.

AIRBM — Anti-intermediate-range-ballistic-missile.

AIRCOM—U.S. Air Force communications complex.

AIRCOMNET—U.S. Air Force Communications Network.

AIROPNET—U.S. Air Force Operational Network.

AISE—Association of Iron and Steel Engineers.

AITA—Air Industries and Transports Association.

AIUS—Man-in-Space International Association.

AIWI—American Industrial Writing Institute.

AJ—Alloy Junction. Antijam (radar term).

AK—Amplitude-keyed. Automatic clock. Cargo ship (U.S. Navy).

AKS—General store issue ship (U.S. Navy).

AKV—Aircraft ferry (U.S. Navy).

AL—Aeronautical radio navigation land station (ITU designation). Aviation electronicsman (U.S. Navy).

ALARM—Automatic light aircraft readiness monitor (developed by Bendix Corp., York, Pa.).

ALBM—Air-launched ballistic missile.

ALC—Automatic level control. Automatic load control.

ALCEA—Airline Communication Employees' Association.

ALCH—Approach light contact height.

ALCOM—Algebraic compiler.

ALD—Acceptable limit for sample dispersion.

ALDA—Airline Dispatchers' Association.

ALERT—Automatic-logging electronic reporting and telemetering (developed by RCA).

ALF—Alphanumeric. Automatic letter facer.

ALFA—Air-lubricated free-attitude trainer.

ALGM—Air-launched guided missile.

ALGO—Algebraic compiler based on international algol (program for the Bendix G-15 computer).

ALGOL—Algorithmic language.

ALICE—Adiabatic, low-energy injection and capture experiment (Lawrence Radiation Laboratory). Alaska integrated communications exchange.

ALIT—Automatic line insulation test (tester).

ALM—Air-launched missile.

ALMAJCOM—All major command letters.

ALO—Air liaison officer.

ALPR—Argonne low-power reactor.

ALPS—Advanced liquid propulsion system (developed by Jet Propulsion Laboratory).

AL PUR COM—All purpose communications system (developed by Automation Management, Inc., and Alden Electronic and Impulse Recording Equipment Co.).

ALRI—Airborne long-range input (U.S. Air Force program).

ALRIC—Airborne long-range input electronic (developed by Burroughs Corp.).

ALS—Automatic landing system.

ALT—Alternate.

ALTAC—Algebraic translator and compiler.

ALTARE—Automatic logic testing and recording equipment (developed by Autonetics, Downey, Calif.).

ALTREC—Automatic life testing and recording of electronic components (manufactured by Canadian Marconi).

ALU—Arithmetic and logic unit.

AM—Air ministry (British). Ammeter (JIC and NMTBA term). Amplifier (JAN nomenclature). Amplitude modulation. Ante meridian. Auxiliary memory. Minesweeper (U.S. Navy).

A/M—Auto-manual.

AMA—Academy of Model Aeronautics (1025 Connecticut Ave., N.W., Washington 6, D.C.). Air materiel area. American Management Association. American Medical Association. American Municipal Association. Amplitron amplifier. Automatic message accounting.

AMAL—Aviation Medical Acceleration Laboratory (U.S. Navy).

AMB—Airways Modernization Board (predecessor to Federal Aviation Agency).

AMC—Air Materiel Command. Army Medical Center. Army Medical Corps.

AMCA—Air Moving and Conditioning Association.

AMCCOMNET—Air Materiel Command Communications Network.

AMD—Aerospace Medical Division (U.S. Air Force). Air movement data. Air-moving device. Allied (or American) Military Government. Army's Manhattan District (project for developing the atomic bomb during World War II).

AMDC—Army Missile Development Center (Redstone Arsenal).

AM-DSB—Amplitude modulation, double-sideband.

AM-DSB/SC—Amplitude modulation, double-sideband, suppressed carrier.

AME—Angle-measuring equipment. Anti-multipath equipment.

AMERSTD—American Standard.

AMES—Air Ministry Experimental Station (British ground radar station).

AMH—Alaska Military Highway.

AMIS—Air movements information service.

AMIS SCRIPT—Flight plan information book (SAGE term).

AML—Aeronautical Materials Laboratory (Naval Air Material Center, Philadelphia, Pa.). Applied Mathematics Laboratory (David Taylor Model Basin, U.S. Navy, Bureau of Ships).

AMM—Antimissile missile.

AMMI—American Merchant Marine Institute.

AMMO—Army mobile missile operation.

AMMSDO—Antimissile missile and space defense office.

AMOS—ARPA Midcourse Observatory Site. (Maui, Hawaii). Automatic Meteorological Observation Station (U.S. Weather Bureau).

AMP—Add, multiprecision. **[Cont.]**

17

Amplifier. Army mine planter.

AMPAS—Academy of Motion Picture Arts and Sciences.

AMPH—Amphibian. Amphibious.

AMP-HR—Ampere-hour.

AMPL—Amplifier.

AMPLAS—Apparatus mounted in plastic.

AMPS—Army mine planter service. Automatic message-processing system.

AMR—Airborne magnetic recorder. Atlantic missile range. Automatic message-registering.

AMRI—Association of Missile and Rocket Industries.

AMRL—Army Medical Research Laboratory (Ft. Knox, Ky.).

AMROO—Atlantic Missile Range Operations Office.

AMS—Army Map Service. Army Medical Staff.

AMSA—American Metal Stamping Association.

AMSL—Above mean sea level.

AMSOC—American Miscellaneous Society (a committee of the National Academy of Sciences).

AMSS—Automatic master sequence selector.

AM-SSB—Amplitude modulation, single-sideband, suppressed carrier.

AMST—Association of Maximum Service Telecasters, Inc.

AMTEC—Automatic time-element compensator (developed by Ampex Corp.).

AMTDA—American Machine Tool Distributors' Association.

AMTI—Airborne moving target indicator.

A/M/T/S—Auto Manual Test Service.

AMV—Astable mutivibrator.

AMVER—Atlantic Merchant Vessel Report.

AN—Air Force-Navy Aeronautical.

Net-laying ship (U.S. Navy).

ANA—Aerojet network analyzer.

ANACOM—Analog computer.

ANATRON—Analog translator.

ANC—Air Navigation Conference. All-number calling.

ANCLAV—Automatic navigation computer for land and amphibious vehicles (developed by Ford Instrument Div. of Sperry Rand Corp. for the Army).

ANCOR—Angle extrusion and corner casting.

ANDB—Air Navigation Development Board.

ANI—Automatic number identification (telephone term).

ANIAI—National Association of Italian Engineers and Architects.

ANIP—Army-Navy Instrumentation Program.

ANIPLA—Italian Society for Automatic Control.

ANL—Argonne National Laboratory (Atomic Energy Commission).

ANMB—Army and Navy Munitions Board.

ANMCC—Alternate national military command center.

ANNA—Army - NASA - Navy - Air Force (geodetic satellite program).

ANOVA—Analysis of variance.

ANP—Aircraft nuclear propulsion.

ANPO—Office for Aircraft Nuclear Propulsion.

ANPP—Aircraft nuclear propulsion program. Army nuclear power program.

ANS—American Nuclear Society. Automatic navigation system.

ANSAM—Antimissile surface-to-air missile.

ANT—Antenna.

ANTAC—Air navigation and tactical system.

ANTC—Air navigation traffic control.

ANWCG—Army Nuclear Weapon Coordination Group (Ft. Belvoir, Va.).

AO—Amplifier output. Oil tanker (U. S. Navy). Astronomical Observatory.

AOA—American Ordnance Association (Mills Bldg., Washington 6, D.C.). Angle of attack.

AOAC—Army Ordnance Ammunition Center (Joliet, Ill.). Army Ordnance Ammunition Command.

A-O-AMPL—And-or-amplifier.

AOB—Angle of bank.

AOC—Air operations center. Army Ordnance Corps. Automatic output control. Automatic overload control.

AOCP—Airplane out of commission for parts.

AOG—Gasoline tanker (U.S. Navy).

AOGM—Accelerated optimum gradient method.

AOGMS—Army Ordnance Guided Missile School (Redstone Arsenal, Huntsville, Ala.).

AOIT—Automatic outgoing intertoll trunk-test circuit.

AOMC—Army Ordnance Missile Command.

AOMSA—Army Ordnance Missile Support Agency.

AOPA—Aircraft Owners' and Pilots' Association.

AOQL—Average outgoing quality limit.

AOS—Add-or-subtract.

AOSO—Advanced orbiting solar observatory.

AOU—Azimuth orientation unit.

AP—Attack plotter. Transport (U.S. Navy).

APAAU—Army personnel assigned to amphibious units.

APAC—Airborne parabolic arc computer (developed by Nortronic Div. of Northrop). Airesearch pneumatic analog computer.

APADS—Automatic programmer and data system (developed by Lockheed).

APATS—Automatic programmer and test system.

APB—Barracks ship (U.S. Navy).

APBE—Association for Professional Broadcasting Education.

APC—Adjustable-pressure conveyor. Alien property custodian. Analog-to-pressure converter. Army Pictorial Center (Long Island City, N.Y.). Automatic phase control.

APCH—Approach.

APCHE—Automatic programmed checkout equipment.

APCO—Associated Police Communications Officers, Inc.

APD—Air procurement district. Analog-to-pulse duration. Angular position digitizer. Association of Professional Draftsmen. Ex-destroyer high-speed transport (U.S. Navy).

APDA—American Power Dispatchers' Association, Inc.

APE—Automatic positioning equipment (developed by Shell Oil).

APEO—Association of Professional Engineers of Ontario, Canada.

APEP—Association of Professional Engineering Personnel (union of engineers).

APF—Administrative flagship (U.S. Navy).

APG—Aberdeen Proving Grounds (U.S. Army Ordnance). Supporting gunnery ship (U.S. Navy).

APGC—Air Proving Ground Center (Eglin Air Force Base, Fla.).

APH—Transport ship for evacuation of wounded (U. S. Navy).

API—Air-position indicator. American Petroleum Institute.

APIC—Automatic power-input controller.

APICS—American Production and Inventory Control Society **[Cont.]**

(330 S. Wells St., Chicago 6. Ill.)

APJA—Appliance Parts Jobbers' Association.

APL—Automatic phase lock. Average picture level. Labor transport ship (U.S. Navy).

APM—Antipersonnel missile. Mechanized artillery transport (U.S. Navy).

APMI—American Powder Metallurgy Institute (60 E. 42nd St., New York 17, N. Y.).

APN—Nonmechanized artillery transport.

APO—Air Procurement Office. Army Post Office.

APOD—Aerial port of debarkation.

APOE—Aerial port of embarkation.

APOTA—Automatic positioning telemetering antenna.

APP—Approach control office. Automatic plate processor (storage device in Bell Labs electronic central office equipment). Automatic position planning. Auxiliary power plant.

APPA—American Public Power Association.

APPC—Automatic power-plant checker (used for MACE missile).

APPECS—Adaptive pattern-perceiving electronic computer system (developed by General Dynamics).

APPR—Army package power reactor.

APR—Automatic production recording. Rescue transport (U.S. Navy).

APRIL—Automatically programmed remote indication logging (manufactured by General Electric).

APRT—Airport.

APRXLY—Approximately.

APS—American Physical Society. Assimilations per second (term used in illumination work). Automatic pilot systems. Auxiliary power system.

APT—Automatic picture transmis-

sion.

APTI—Actions-per-time-interval.

APTS—Automatic picture transmission system.

APU—Army postal unit. Audio playback unit. Auxiliary power unit.

APUHS—Automatic program unit, high-speed.

APULS—Automatic program unit, low-speed.

APV—Aircraft transport (U. S. Navy).

AQ—Any quantity.

AQGV—Azimuth quantized gated video.

AQL—Acceptable quality level.

AR—Acoustic reflex. Acquisition radar. Action register. Aeronautical radio navigation. Amateur radio (ITU designation). Amplifier. Area of resolution. Armored reconnaissance. Army. Army regulations. Aromatic. Repair ship (U. S. Navy).

ARA—Agricultural Research Administration.

ARAD—Airborne radar and doppler position system.

ARADCOM—Air Defense Command (U.S. Army).

ARB—Aircraft reactors branch. Repair ship-battle damage (U. S. Navy).

ARBA—American Road Builders' Association.

ARBOR—Argonne boiling reactor experiment.

ARC—Automatic range control (developed by Bendix). Automatic ratio control. Analyzer-recorder-controller. Cable repairing or laying ship (U.S. Navy).

ARCAS—All-purpose rocket for collecting atmospheric soundings (made for Office of Naval Research by Atlantic Research Corp.). Automatic radar chain acquisition system (developed by Cubic Corp.).

ARCH—Articulated computing hierarchy (developed by Elliott Automation Ltd., England).

ARCON—Automatic rudder control.

ARD—Floating dry dock (U.S. Navy).

ARDA—Analog recording dynamic analyzer (developed by Digital Dynamics, Inc.).

ARDC—Air Research and Development Command. Repair dock (U. S. Navy).

ARDS—Aviation Research and Development Service (Federal Aviation Agency).

ARE—Aircraft reactor experiment.

AREA—Amateur Radio Emergency Association. American Railway Engineering Association.

AREC—Advanced Rocket Engineering Club (1519 E. Pastorius St., Philadelphia, Pa.).

ARENTS—Advanced research environmental test satellite.

ARF—Aeronautical Research Foundation. Armour Research Foundation.

ARFC—Average rectified forward current.

ARFCOS—Armed Forces Courier Service.

ARGE—Arbeitgemeinschaft (West German manufacturing combine).

ARGMA—Army Rocket and Guided Missile Agency.

ARGONAUT—Argonne's reactor for university training.

ARGP—Aeronautical radionavigation glide path.

ARGUS—Automatic routine generating and updating system (developed by Minneapolis Honeywell for its Model 800 computer).

ARI—Air Conditioning and Refrigeration Institute (1346 Connecticut Ave. N.W., Washington 6. D.C.).

ARIP—Automatic rocket impact predictor.

ARIS—Advance range instrumentation ship (formerly called Mars—Mobile Atlantic Range Station).

ARL—Acceptable reliability levels. Admiralty Research Laboratory (England). Aerial Reconnaissance Lab (U.S. Air Force—Wright Air Development Center). Association of Research Libraries.

ARLI—Airborne long-range input (U.S. Air Force).

ARLIS—Arctic Laboratory Ice Station (U. S. Navy, Office of Naval Research).

ARM—Amateur radio monitor. Antiradar missile (U.S. Air Force project).

ARMA—American Records Management Association (3365 Middlebury Dr., Dearborn, Mich.).

ARMF—Advanced reactivity measurement facility.

ARMS—Aerial radiological monitoring system.

ARO—Applied research objectives. Army Research Office.

ARP—Airborne radar platform.

ARPA—Advanced Research Projects Agency.

ARPAT—Advanced Research Projects Agency's Terminal.

ARPO—Aerial Phenomenal Research Organization. Applied research program.

ARQ—Automatic error correction. Automatic request. Automatic requesting telegraph.

ARR—Aeronautical radionavigation radar. Anti-repeat relay.

ARRC—Air Reserve Records Center (Denver, Colo.).

ARRL—American Radio Relay League (U.S. association of radio amateurs).

ARS—Advanced reconnaissance satellite (also known as Pied **[Cont.]**

Piper and WS-117L). **Air Rescue Service.** American Rocket Society. Salvage ship (U.S. Navy).

ARSR—Air route surveillance radar.

ARST- –Aerial reconnaissance and security troop.

ART—Advanced research and technology. Airborne radiation thermometer. Arc-resistance testers. Automatic reporting telephone (telephone term).

ARTC—Air route traffic control.

ARTCC—Air route traffic control center.

ARTOC—Army Tactical Operations Central (Developed by Aeronutronics Div., Ford Motor Co.).

ARTRON—Artificial neuron.

ARTS—Annual Research Task Summary (published by Office of Technical Services, U.S. Dept. of Commerce, Washington 25, D.C.). Army Research Task Summary. Associated Radio and TV Servicemen (Chicago).

ARU—Acoustic resistance unit.

ARV—Aircraft repair ship (U.S. Navy).

AS—Add-subtract. Antenna assembly (JAN nomenclature). Antisubmarine. Submarine tender (U.S. Navy).

ASA—Acoustical Society of America (57 E. 55th St., New York 17, N.Y.). American Standards Association. American Statistical Association. Army Security Agency.

ASAP—Analog system assembly pack (developed by Embree Electronics Corp.).

ASB—Air Safety Board.

ASBCA—Armed Services Board of Contract Appeals.

ASC—Aeronautical systems center (Air Materiel Command, Wright Field). Army Signal Corps. Army Specialist Corps. Astronautical Society of Canada. Automatic

sensitivity control.

ASCAT—Analog self-checking automatic tester (developed by Bell Aircraft, 1959).

ASCC—Air Standardization Coordinating Committee.

ASCE—American Society of Civil Engineers.

ASCS—Automatic stabilization and control system.

ASD—Aeronautical Systems Division (U.S. Air Force).

ASDE—Airport surface detection equipment (developed by Airborne Instruments Laboratory).

ASDEFORLANT — Antisubmarine Defense Force, Atlantic Fleet (U.S. Naval Base, Norfolk 11, Va.).

ASDEFORPAC—Antisubmarine Defense Force, Pacific Fleet (U.S. Navy).

ASDG—Antisubmarine Defense Group.

ASDIC—Allied Submarine Devices Investigation Committee. Armed Services Documents Intelligence Center.

ASDO—Aviation Safety Agent District Office.

ASD(R&D)—Assistant Secretary of Defense for Research and Development.

ASD(S&L)—Assistant Secretary of Defense for Supply and Logistics.

ASE—Aerospace support equipment. American Society of Engineers. Automatic stabilization equipment (developed by Sikorsky). Service entrance cable, protected type.

ASECNA—Agency for Air Navigation Security in Africa and Madagascar.

ASEE—American Society for Engineering Education.

ASER—Amplification by stimulated emission of radiation.

ASESA—Armed Services Electrostandards Agency (U.S. Signal Corps, Ft. Monmouth, N.J.).

ASETC—Armed Services Electron Tube Committee.

ASF—Army Service Forces.

ASFIR—Active swept frequency interferometer radar.

ASFTCU—Army Service Forces Training Center Units.

ASG—Aeronautical Standards Group. Army Surgeon General.

ASH—Assault support helicopter.

ASHAE—American Society of Heating and Air Conditioning Engineers.

ASHR—Airborne height-surveillance radar.

ASI—Anti-saturation inverter.

ASID—Automatic station identification device.

ASII—American Science Information Institute (2602 David Stott Bldg., Detroit 26, Mich.).

ASIPRE—Army Snow, Ice and Permafrost Research Establishment (U.S. Army Dept.).

ASIS—Abort sensing and implementation system.

ASL—Association of Standards Laboratories.

ASLE—American Society of Lubrication Engineers (5 N. Wabash Ave., Chicago 2, Ill.).

ASLIB—Association of Special Libraries and Information Bureaux (London).

ASLO—American Society of Limnology and Oceanography.

ASM—Air-to-surface missile. American Society for Metal.

ASME—American Society of Mechanical Engineers.

ASMI—Airfield surface movement indicator (manufactured by Decca Radar Ltd.).

ASN—Army serial number. Average sample number.

ASNE—American Society of Naval Engineers.

ASO—Administrative Service Office. Air Surveillance Officer. Aviation Supply Office (Navy Department).

ASP—Aerospace plane. American Society of Photogrammetry (1515 Massachusetts Ave., N.W., Washington, D.C.). Automatic servo plotter. Automatic switching panel.

ASPA—Armed Services Procurement Act.

ASPDE—Automatic shaft-position data encoder.

ASPR—Armed Services Procurement Act Regulations.

ASQC—American Society for Quality Control.

ASR—Airborne surveillance radar. Airport surveillance radar. Automatic sending and receiving. Automatic step regulator. Submarine rescue vessel (U.S. Navy).

ASRA—Automatic stereo recording amplifier.

ASROC—Antisubmarine rocket (developed by Minneapolis-Honeywell and Naval Ordnance Test Station, China Lake).

ASSE—American Society for Safety Engineers.

ASSET—Aerothermodynamic structural systems evaluation test (U.S. Air Force project).

AST—Army specialized training. Atomized suspension technique.

ASTC—Army Satellite Tracking Center (Deal, N.J.—near Ft. Monmouth).

ASTEC—Advanced solar turbo-electric conversion system.

ASTER—Antisubmarine Terrier (prime contractor: Ford Instrument).

ASTIA—Armed Services Technical Information Agency.

ASTM—American Society for Testing Materials.

ASTME—American Society of Tool and Manufacturing Engineers.

ASTOR—Nuclear torpedo.

ASTRA—Adapted swimming - pool tank reactor, Austria. Automatic sorting, testing, recording analysis.

ASTRAC—Arizona statistical repetitive analog computer (developed by University of Arizona, Tucson, Ariz.).

ASTREC—Atomic strike recording complex.

ASTRO—Advanced spacecraft truck /trainer/transport reusable orbiter.

ASTU—Air support training unit. Automatic systems test unit (developed by Esso to test stream analyzers).

ASV—Acceleration-switching valve. Aerothermodynamic/structural vehicle. Air-to-surface vessel.

A-SV—Automatic self-verification.

ASW—Antisubmarine warfare.

ASWEPS—Antisubmarine weapons environmental prediction systems.

AT—Aerial torpedo. Ambient temperature. Ampere-turns. Analysis time. Antenna (JAN nomenclature). Antitank. Astronomical time. Attenuator/pad. Atomic time. Automatic ticketing. Oceangoing fleet tug (U.S. Navy).

A/T—Action time.

ATA—Air Transport Association.

ATABE—Automatic target assignment and battery evaluation.

ATAE—Association of Telephone Answering Exchanges.

ATAS—Academy of TV Arts and Sciences (9126 Sunset Blvd., Los Angeles 46, Calif.).

ATAW—Advanced tactical assault weapon.

ATB—All trunks busy (telephone term).

ATBM—Anti-tactical ballistic missile.

ATC—Air traffic control. Air Training Command. Army Transportation Corps. Automatic tap-changing transformer. Automatic temperature compensation. Automatic train control. Automatic tuning control.

ATCA—Air Traffic Control Association.

ATCBGS—Air Traffic Control Beacon Ground Station.

ATCC—Air Traffic Control Center. Air Traffic Control Communications.

ATCEU—Air traffic control experimental unit (British system).

ATCO—Air Traffic Coordinating Officer.

ATCOM—Air traffic compiler (developed by Applied Data Research, Princeton, N.J.).

ATCRB—Air traffic control beacon.

ATCRBS—Air traffic control radar beacon system.

ATC&W—Air traffic control and aircraft warning.

ATDD—Airship Test and Development Department (U. S. Navy—Lakehurst, N.J.).

ATDS—Air tactical data system.

ATE—Altitude - transmission equipment. Air turbo exchanger. Automatic test equipment.

ATEWA—Automatic target evaluator and weapon assignor.

ATF—Antarctic Task Force. Automatic target follower. Ocean tug (U.S. Navy).

ATHESA—Automatic three-dimensional electronic scanned array (antenna system developed by Sperry).

ATHODYD — Aero-thermodynamic duct (a ramjet engine).

ATIC—Air Technical Intelligence Center.

ATILO—Air Technical and Intelligence Liaison Officer.

ATL—Automatic test line (telephone term).

ATM—Antitank missile. Arc-tangent mechanism. Atmosphere.

ATMOS—Atmospheric.

ATO—Aeronautical telecommunications operator. Air Tactics Officer. Area Traffic Officer. Assist take-off.

ATOT—Angle track on target.

ATP—Actual time of penetration.

ATPS—Automatic type placement system (automatic equipment for map making).

ATR—Advanced test reactor. Air turborocket. Anti-transmit-receive.

ATRAN—Automatic terrain recognition and navigation.

ATS—Air Tactical School. Air Traffic Services. American Television Society.

ATSG—Teflon (fused tape), shield, silicone-impregnated fiber glass (cable).

ATSJ—Teflon (fused tape), shield, teflon jacket (cable).

ATSS—Acquisition and tracking subsystem.

ATW—Air Transport Wing.

AU—Air University (U.S. Air Force). Angstrom units. Astronomical unit (the mean distance from the earth to the sun). Automatic (NMTBA term).

AUDAR—Autodyne detection and ranging.

AUDIT—Automatic unattended detection inspection transmitter (monitors nuclear tests).

AUDITRON—Audio information transducer (developed by Bulova, Queens, N.Y.).

AUDREY—Automatic digit recognizer (voice-actuated machine built by Bell Labs; distinguishes 10 spoken digits).

AUET—Armored, universal engineer tractor.

AUM—Air-to-underwater missile.

AUS—Army of the United States.

AUSA—Association of the United States Army.

AUSCOR—Automatic scanning correlator (Canadian development for mapping).

AUTEC—Atlantic underwater test and evaluation center.

AUTO ANN—Automatic announce.

AUTOMAP—Automatic machining program (developed by IBM).

AUTOPIC—Automated personal identification code (developed by IBM).

AUTOPROMPT—Automatic programming of machine tools.

AUTOSPOT—Automatic system for positioning tools (developed by IBM).

AUX—Auxiliary.

AV—Anion vacancies. Auriculoventricular. Seaplane tender (U.S. Navy).

AVA—Active Van Atta array (antenna system).

AVB—Asbestos and varnished cambric, flame-retardant, cotton braid (wire).

AVC—Asbestos, varnished-cambric (wire and cable). Automatic volume control.

AvCIR—Aviation Crash Injury Research (division of Flight Safety Foundation, Phoenix, Ariz.).

AVCS—Advanced vidicon camera system (developed by RCA).

AVD—Automatic voice data.

AVE—Automatic volume expansion.

AvF—Availability factor.

AVG—Escort ship—aircraft (U.S. Navy).

AVL—Approved vendors list. Asbestos and varnished cambric—wet locations (wire).

AVNL—Automatic video noise limiting.

AVPD—Heat- and moisture-resistant cord.

AVPO—Heat- and moisture-resistant cord.

AVR—Aircraft rescue ship (U.S. Navy). Automatic voice relay (developed by Cook Electric Co.).

AVS—Adjustable voltage screwdowns. American Vacuum Society.

AVSEP—Audio-visual superimposed electrocardiogram presentation (developed by Avionics Research Corp., Los Angeles 45, Calif.).

AVT—Aerodynamically variable throat. Air velocity transducer. Applications vertical test.

AW—Aircraft warning. Automatic word. Distilling ship (U.S. Navy).

AWA—Aviation Writers' Association.

AWC—Army War College. Army Weapons Command.

AWCS—Airborne weapons control system (designed by RCA for U.S. Air Force F-102). Automatic warning and control systems.

AWG—American wire gauge.

AWK—Water tanker (U.S. Navy).

AWLS—All-weather landing system.

AWRS—Airborne weather radar system.

AWRTV—American Women in Radio and TV.

AWS—Air Weather Service (U.S. Air Force). Aircraft Warning Service. Aircraft warning set. American Welding Society (33 N. 39th St., New York 18, N.Y.).

AYI—Angle-of-yaw indicator.

AZ—Airship tender (U.S. Navy). Azimuth.

AZAN—Azimuth and range data.

AZAR—Adjustable-zero adjustable-range.

AZ-EL—Azimuth - elevation (modified type of PPI presentation).

B

B—Balloon ceiling (weather-report term). Bar. Barn (10^{-24} cm²). Bias. Beam unit (used as subscript). Bel. Bit. Blower. Brake relay (NMTBA term). Branch. Burner flame. Communications (U.S. Air Force mission designation). Synchro.

BA—Battery—primary type (JAN nomenclature). Binary add.

BABS—Blide approach beacon system.

BAC—Barometric altitude controller. Binary asymmetric channel.

BACE—Basic automatic checkout equipment. British Association of Consulting Engineers.

BADC—Binary asymmetric dependent channel.

BADGE—Base area defense ground environment (radar system manufactured by General Electric Co., Syracuse, N.Y.).

BAE—British Admiralty Establishment.

BAIC—Binary asymmetric independent channel.

BALAST—Balloon astronomy.

BALGOL — Burroughs algebraic compiler.

BALOP—Balopticon.

BAM—Broadcasting AM.

BAMBI—Ballistic antimissile boost intercept.

BANIR—Bantam inertial reference (used in the GE "Bantam" avionic system).

BAP — Band amplitude product (bandwidth times maximum peak-to-peak amplitude).

BAR—Buffer address register.

BARLANT—Atlantic Barrier Patrol

(eastern seaward extension of the dew line).

BARO FUZE—Barometric fuze.

BARPAC—Pacific Barrier Patrol (western seaward extension of the DEW line).

BASIC—Basic appraisal system for incoming components. Battle area surveillance and integrated communications (developed by Stromberg-Carlson for the U.S. Marine Corps). Biological abstract subjects in context.

BASICO—Biological Abstracts, un Servicio de Information Cientifica Organizada.

BASICPAC—Basic processor and computer (medium-size, general-purpose computer designed by Philco).

BASOPS—Base Operations Office.

BAT—Battery.

BB—Battery—secondary type (JAN nomenclature). Breaker block. Browning-Bledsoe (pattern recognition scheme).

BBC—British Broadcasting Corp.

BBCRD—British Broadcasting Company Research Department.

BBG—Board of Broadcasting Governors (Canadian organization similar to FCC).

bbl—Barrel.

BBM—Break-before-make.

BC—Bare copper. Base sleeve. Bathyconductograph. Bayonet cap (standard twin contact). Binary code. Binary counter. Boro-carbon. Broadcasting station (ITU designation).

BCAC—British Conference on Automation and Computation.

BCB—Broadcast band.

BCC—Battery control center. Body centered cubic.

BCD—Binary coded decimal.

BCD/B—Binary coded decimal/binary.

BCD/Q—Binary coded decimal/quaternary.

BCF—Bureau of Commercial Fisheries (U.S. Department of the Interior). FM broadcasting station (ITU designation).

BCFSK—Binary code frequency shift keying.

BCG—Ballistocardiogram.

BCI—Broadcast interference.

BCIU—Business Council for International Understanding (organization for providing training for business and technical men going abroad).

BCN—Beacon.

BCO—Binary coded octal.

BCOI—British Central Office of Information.

BCS — Bardeen - Cooper - Schrieffer (theory of superconductivity). British Computer Society.

BCSE—Board of Civil Service Examiners.

BCST—Broadcast.

BCT—TV broadcasting station (ITU designation).

BD—Bernoulli disk (rotating magnetic-disk storage device). Binary decode. Binary divide.

BDA—Booster-distribution amplifier.

BDC—Binary decimal counter.

BDD—Binary-to-decimal decoder.

BDH—Bearing, distance and heading.

BDHI—Bearing, distance, heading indicator.

BDI—Bearing deviation indicator. Biological damage indicator.

BDL—Battery data link.

BDSA—Business and Defense Services Administration (U.S. Department of Commerce).

BE—Band elimination.

Bé—Beaumé.

BEAC—Boeing electronic analog computer.

BEACOTRON — Beam coupling

27

tube.

BEAMA—British Electrical and Allied Manufacturers' Association (36-38 Kingsway, London W.C. 2, England).

BEC—Boston Engineers' Club.

BECEG—Bureau European de Controle et d'Etudes Generales (European common market engineers' group).

BECO—Booster engine cutoff.

BEMA—Business Equipment Manufacturers' Association.

BENITO—CW navigational system.

BEPO—British experimental pile.

BEPOC—Burroughs electrographic printer-plotter for ordnance computing (developed by Burroughs Corp.).

BEQ—Ballistocardiograph.

BESS—Binary electromagnetic signal signature.

BEST—Better Electronic Service Technicians (Arizona organization of TV servicemen).

BET—Brunauer-Emmet-Teller (surface investigation of platinum-carbon catalysts).

BeV—Billion electron-volts.

BF—Basse frequence (French term). Beam-forming.

BFB—Bundesverband der Freien Berufe (association of free professions—German).

BFC—Bureau of Foreign Commerce (U.S. Department of Commerce).

BFM—Barium ferrite magnet.

BFO—Beat frequency oscillator.

BG—Birmington gauge.

BGE—Butyl glycidyl ether.

BHP—Brake horsepower.

BHS—Basic hole system.

Bi—Biot.

BIAX—Biaxial magnetic field computer element.

BIBO—Bureau of International Business Operations (U.S. Department of Commerce).

BIC—Bombardment-induced conductivity.

BIDEC—Binary-to-decimal.

BIDEMATRON — Injected-beam distributed - emission magnetron amplifier.

BIEE—British Institute of Electrical Engineers.

BIFR—Before encountering instrument flight rules condition (CAA term).

BIL—Basic impulse insulation level.

BILB—Built-in light beacon.

BILE—Balanced inductor logical element (developed by IBM).

BIMATRON—Injected-beam magnetron amplifier.

BIMCAM—British Industrial Measuring and Control Apparatus Manufacturers' Association.

BIO—Biological Information - Processing Organization.

BIOR—Business input-output rerun.

BIOS—Biological investigations of space.

BIPAD—Binary pattern detector.

BIPCO—Built-in-place components (developed by Burroughs Corp.).

BIRDIE—Battery integration and radar display equipment (manufactured by Martin Co., for U.S. Army Signal Corps).

BIRE—British Institute of Radio Engineers.

BIS—British Interplanetary Society.

BISITS—British Iron and Steel Industry Translation Service.

BISRA—British Iron and Steel Research Association.

BIT—Binary digit. Built-in-test.

BITN—Bilateral iterative network.

BIVAR—Bivariant function generator (manufactured by Electronic Associates, Inc.).

BIX—Binary information exchange.

BJ—Barrage jamming.

BL—Blanking. Bombline.

BLACKMARI—Air-to-air identification system (developed by the United Kingdom).

BLADE—Base level automation of data through electronics (Air Force data-processing project). Bell Laboratories automatic design (computer for use in Nike-Zeus missile system).

BLADES—Bell Laboratories automatic design system.

BLC—Boundary layer control. British Lighting Council.

BLEU—Blind landing experimental unit (developed by Royal Aircraft Establishment, Farnsborough, England—British Air Traffic Control System).

BLIP—Background-limited infrared photoconductor.

BLK—Black.

BLLE—Balanced NNE logical element (developed by IBM).

BLODI—Block diagram compiler.

BLPZZ—Bent logarithmically periodic zig-zags.

BLS—Bureau of Labor Statistics.

BLST—Ballast.

BLT—Blanket.

BM—Ballistic missile. Binary multiply. Boatswain's mate (U.S. Navy). Brightness merit. Buffer module.

BMC—Ballistic missile center (U.S. Air Force). Basic missile checker (used for MACE missile).

BMCO—Ballistic Missile Construction Office (Division of U.S. Corps of Army Engineers).

BMD—Ballistic Missile Division (Air Research and Development Command, Inglewood, Calif.). Bomber defense missile.

BMDC—Ballistic Missile Defense Committee.

BMDS—Ballistic missile defense system.

BMEWS—Ballistic missile early warning system.

BMI—Ballistic missile interceptor.

BMO—Ballistic Missile Office (Air Materiel Command, Inglewood, Calif.).

BMS—British Ministry of Supply.

BMSO—Blue Mountains Seismological Observatory (Baker, Oregon).

BMSRDE—British Ministry of Supply Research and Development Establishment.

BN—Binary number system.

BNDDIS—Band display.

BNFMRA—British Nonferrous Metals Research Association.

BNL—Brookhaven National Laboratory (U.S. Atomic Energy Commission).

BNP—Bureau of Naval Personnel.

BNU—Basic-notch-unit.

BNW—Bureau of Naval Weapons Main Navy Building, Washington 25, D.C.).

BO—Beat oscillator. Blocking oscillator. Branch out. Bureau of Ordnance.

BOA—Broad ocean area.

BOASI—Bureau of Old Age and Survivors Insurance.

BOB—Bureau of the Budget.

BOD—Biological oxygen demand.

BOF—Barium oxide ferrite.

BOFTE—Bureau of Ordnance Fleet Test Equipment.

BOLT—Beam-of-light transistor.

BOM—Bill of material.

BONUS—Boiling nuclear superheat reactor. Bows or north up stabilized.

BOP—Burnout-proof.

BOQ—Bachelor officers' quarters.

BORAX—Boiling water reactor experiment (NRTS, Idaho).

BOREQ—Broadcast requested.

BOSS—Bioastronautical orbiting satellite (NASA project). Bomb orbital strategic systems (U.S. Air Force project).

BOVC—Base of overcast (CAA term).

BP—Band pass. Boiling point. Boron plastic. Broadcast Pioneers (association of persons with long years of service in radio).

BPA—Bonneville Power Administration.

BPF—Bandpass filter. Bromine pentafluoride (rocket propellant oxidant).

bpi—Bits per inch.

BPMS—Blood-pressure measuring system.

BPO—British Post Office.

BPOC—Before proceeding on course (CAA term).

BPR—Bureau of Public Roads.

bps—Bits per second.

BPU—Basic-pole-unit.

BR—Brake relay (JIC term).

BRAMATEC—Brain-mapping techniques.

BRANE—Bombing radar and navigation equipment (IBM system used on B-52).

BRD—Bellofram rolling diaphragm.

BRG—Bearing.

BRI—Building Research Institute.

BRIL—Brilliance.

BRIT—Blast and residual initial and thermal radiation.

BRIT IRE—British Institute of Radio Engineers.

BRL—Ballistic Research Laboratories (U.S. Army Ordnance, Aberdeen Proving Ground, Md.). Bomb release line.

BRLESC—Ballistic Research Laboratories electronic scientific computer (Ballistic Research Laboratories, U.S. Army Ordnance, Aberdeen Proving Ground, Md.).

BRM—Barometer.

BroFiCon—Broadcast Fighter Control.

BRS—Business Radio Service.

BRVMA—British Radio Valve Manufacturers' Association.

BS—Base shell. Binary subtract. Biometric Society. British Standard.

B & S—Brown & Sharpe (wire gauge).

BSC—Backspace contact. Base Message Switching Center. Binary symmetric channel.

BSD—Ballistics Systems Division (U.S. Air Force SC). Burst slug detection (nuclear term).

BSDC—Binary symmetric dependent channel.

BSF—Bulk shielding facility.

BSI—British Standards Institution.

BSIC—Binary symmetric independent channel.

BSIRA—British Scientific Instrument Research Association.

BSR—Bulk shielding reactor (Oak Ridge, Tenn.).

BSS—Basic shaft system. Bomarc squadron simulator. British standard specifications.

BSSRS—Bureau of Safety and Supply Radio Services (an FCC bureau).

BST—Beam-switching tube.

BS&W—Basic sediment and water.

BT—Bathythermograph. Battery. Boilerman (U.S. Navy).

BTC—Basic Training Center.

BTDL—Back-transient diode logic.

BTI—Bank and turn indicator.

BTO—Bombing through overcast.

BTRY—Battery.

BTST—Busy-tone start lead (telephone term).

BTU—British thermal unit.

BU—Builder (U.S. Navy). Bureau.

BuAer—Bureau of Aeronautics (U.S. Navy).

BUG—Bomarc UNIVAC AN/GPA-35 (digital computer simulator for Bomarc).

BUIC—Backup interceptor control (backup for SAGE system).

BuOrd—Bureau of Ordnance (U.S.

Navy).

BUR—Bureau.

BuSandA—Bureau of Supplies and Accounts (U.S. Navy).

BUSARB—British - United States Amateur Rocket Bureau (53 St. Andrew St., Hertford, Herts., England).

BuShips—Bureau of Ships (U.S. Navy).

BuWeps—Bureau of Naval Weapons.

BuWepsRep — Bureau of Naval Weapons Representative (U.S. Navy).

BV—Breakdown voltage.

BVA—British Radio Valve Manufacturers' Association.

BVP—Bonhoeffer-Vander Pol model.

BVR—Black void reactor.

BW—Biological warfare.

BWA—Backward-wave amplifier.

BWC—Basic weight controller.

BWG—Birmingham wire gauge.

BWO—Backward wave oscillators.

BWPA—Backward-wave parametric amplifier.

BWR—Bandwidth ratio.

BZ—Audible signal device (JAN nomenclature). Blank when zero.

C

C—Airfield facility (FAA designation). Capacitor. Cargo and logistic support (Air Force mission designation). Centi—(prefix: .01 or 10⁻²). Centigrade. Coast. Coffin (Air Force designation). Coil. Compare. Complexity (reliability term). Compute. Computing. Conformity. Conical (pilot bulb designation). Conductivity. Confidential. Consistency. Control. Control article (JAN nomenclature). Controller. Controlling. Core. Correct (yes). Cotton. Coulomb. Curie (a measure of radioactivity). Cycle. Lamp cord. Spring index (mean diameter of coil divided by wire diameter).

CA—Armored cord. Cancel. Candle. Coast artillery. Consonant amplification. Content addressable memory. Control tower (FAA designation). Current address register. Heavy crusier (U.S. Navy). Sonar commutating assembly (JAN nomenclature).

CAA—Civil Aeronautics Administration.

CAB—Captured air bubble. Cellulose acetate butyrate. Civil Aeronautics Board. Collating and binding.

CABMA—Canadian Association of British Manufacturers and Agencies.

CABRA—Copper and Brass Research Association (420 Lexington Ave., New York 17, N.Y.).

CAC—Changing to approach control (CAA term). Clear all channels. Complete address constant. Continental Army command.

CACE—Chicago Association of Consulting Engineers.

CACOM—Chief Aircraft Communicator.

CAC&W—Continental air control and warning.

CAD — Cartridge-actuated device. Compensated avalanche diode (developed by Shockley Transistor Corp.).

CADF—Commutated antenna direction finder (developed by Standard Telephones and Cables Ltd.).

CADIC—Compagnie Afri- **[Cont.]**

caine Des Ingenieurs-Conseils (Belgian—Africa).

CADIN—Continental Air Defense Integration North.

CADIZ—Canadian Air Defense Identification Zone.

CADL—Dyna-Soar communications and data-link subsystem (developed for Air Force by RCA).

CADPO—Communications and data-processing operation.

CADSS—Combined analog - digital systems simulator.

CADW—Civil air defense warning.

CAEA—California Aviation Education Association (P. O. Box 2454, Sacramento 11, Calif.).

CAFD—Contact analog flight display (instrument for display of flight data).

CAG—Guided missile cruiser (U. S. Navy).

CAI—Canadian Aeronautical Institute. Computer analog input.

CAIDO—Chief Advisor, International District Office (CAA term).

CAI/OP—Computer analog input/output.

CAirC—Caribbean Air Command.

CAL—Caliber (ballistics). Calibrate. Calorie. Compressed air loudspeaker. Cornell Aeronautical Laboratory.

CALBR—Calibration.

CAM—Central address memory. Checkout and automatic monitoring. Chief, aircraft maintenance. Civil air mission. Content addressed memory (designed by Scope, Inc., Falls Church, Va.) Cruise and maintain. Cybernetic anthropomorphous machine.

CAMA—Centralized automatic message accounting.

CAMAL—Continuously airborne, missile launching and low-level penetration.

CAN—Correlation air navigator

(precision radar velocity sensor).

CANCEL—Connecticut Aircraft Nuclear Engine Laboratory (Middletown, Conn.—operated by Pratt & Whitney for AEC).

CANDU—Canadian deuterium uranium reactor (nuclear power-generating station—Douglas Point, Canada).

CANEL—Connecticut Advanced Nuclear Engineering Laboratory (Atomic Energy Commission).

CanUKUS—Canada - United Kingdom-United States.

CANUSE—Canadian-United States Eastern Interconnection.

CAP—Capacitor (JIC and NMTBA term). Civil Air Patrol. Combat Air Patrol.

CAP COM—Capsule communications.

CAPP—Contact approach control (CAA term).

CAPPI—Constant-altitude plan-position indicator (designed by Aeronca Mfg. Co., Baltimore, Md.).

CAP SEP—Capsule separated.

CAR—Center for Aging Research (National Institutes of Health). Civil air regulations.

CARC—Chicago Amateur Radio Club.

CARCC—Chicago Area Radio Club Council.

CARDE—Canadian Armament Research and Development Establishment (Valcartier, Quebec).

CARF—Central Altitude Reservation Facility.

CART—Centralized automatic recorder and tester (developed by Texas Instruments, Inc.). Complete automatic reliability testing.

CARTB—Canadian Association of Radio and TV Broadcasters.

CAS—Canadian Astronautical Society. Chief of Air Staff. Collision-avoidance system.

CASA—Cleveland Aerospace Association.

CASD—Carrier Aircraft Service Division.

CASF—Composite Air Strike Force.

CASI—Canadian Aeronautics and Space Institute (Commonwealth Building, 77 Metcalfe St., Ottawa 4, Ontario, Canada).

CASU—Carrier aircraft service unit.

CAT—Centralized automatic testing (developed by Texas Instruments, Inc.). Civil Air Transport. Classical analytic technique. Clear air turbulence. Command and triangulation system. Computer of average transients (developed by Mnemtron Corp.). Current-adjusting type.

CATE—Current ARDC technical efforts.

CATS—Chicago Area Teleprinter Society. Comprehensive analytical test system (developed by Poly-Scientific Corp., Blacksburg, Va.).

CATT—Conveyorized automatic tube tester (CRT tester developed by National Video Corp.).

CATV—Community antenna TV system.

CAUTRA—Coordinateur Automatique de Traffic (French semiautomatic air traffic control).

CAV—Constant angular velocity.

CAWS—Common aviation weather system.

CAX—Community automatic exchange.

CB—Capacitor bank (JAN nomenclature). Circuit breaker (JIC and NMTBA term). Citizens band. Common base. Common battery. Construction Battalion — Seabees (U.S. Navy). Large cruiser (U.S. Navy).

Cb—Centibels. Coulomb.

CBA—Chemical bond approach. Chesapeake Bay Annex (USNRL).

CBC—Canadian Broadcasting Corp.

CBCC—Common bias, common control.

CBI—Compound batch identification.

CBM—Continental ballistic missile.

CBR—Chemical-biological-radiological.

CBSC—Common bias, single control.

CB&T—Cloud base and top (weather radars).

CC—Carriage control. Central control. Cirrocumulus (meteorological term). Code converter. Coin-collect (telephone term). Combat center. Common carrier. Company commander. Compute orthocount. Computer calculator. Connecting circuit (teletype term). Connector circuit (telephone term). Control center. Control connector. Cross correlation. Cross-coupling. Crystal control.

C&C—Command and control.

CCA—California Circuits Association. Carrier-controlled approach (Ferranti radar for aircraft carrier landing). Cancel corridor assignment (CAA term). Carrier-controlled approach (Navy air traffic control system).

CCB—Convertible circuit breaker.

CCBA—Central Canada Broadcasters' Association.

CCBS—Clear Channel Broadcasting Service (532 Shoreham Bldg., Washington 5, D.C.).

CCCF—Central Committee on Communications Facilities (American Petroleum Institute).

CCD—City (or County) Civil Defense Director. Cold cathode discharge. Combat Center Director.

CCDC—Cape Cod Direction Center (SAGE system).

CCDD—Command Control Development Division (U. S. Air Force, Hanscom Field, Bedford, Mass.).

CCDSO—Command and Control Defense Systems Office.

CCHEP—Cement - coated heavy epoxy.

CCIR—International Radio Consultative Committee.

CCIS—Command control information system.

CCITT—Comite Consultatif International **Telegraphic et Telephonique** (International Telegraph and Telephone Consultative Committee).

CCM — Commodity Class Manager Counter-countermeasures.

CCMD — Continuous **current-monitoring device.**

CCMR—Central Contract Management Region (Wright-Patterson Air Force Base, Ohio).

CCMTA—Cape Canaveral Missile Test Annex.

CCNT—Chief Controller.

CCO—Current-controlled oscillator.

CCPE—Canadian Council of Professional Engineers.

CCPF—Commander-in-Chief, Pacific Fleet.

CCPG—Chemical Corps Proving Ground (U. S. Army, Dugway, Utah).

CCR—Consumable-case solid rocket. Control-circuit resistance.

CCS—Cape Cod system (SAGE system). Cast carbon steel. Collective call sign. Combined Chiefs of Staff. Continuous Commercial Service. Hundred call-seconds.

CC&S—Central computer and sequencer.

CC-SCE—Cumulative composite rating.

CCSEP—Cement-coated single epoxy (magnet wire).

CCTEP—Cement coated triple epoxy.

CCTS—Combat Crew Training School.

CCTV—Closed-circuit television.

CCU—Camera control unit.

CCW—Counterclockwise.

CCWO—Cryptocenter Watch Officer.

CD—Capacitor - diode. Card. Civil Defense. Clock driver. Crystal diode. Current driver. Driver (U. S. Navy).

cd—Candles.

CDA—Civil Defense Agency. Command and data acquisition.

CDB—Combat Development Branch (Signal Corps).

CDC—Call - directing characters (teletype term). Call - directing code. Code-directing character. Command and data-handling console.

CDCE—Central data - conversion equipment.

CDEC—Combat Development Experimental Center (Ft. Ord, Calif.).

CDED — Combat Development Experimental Center (Ft. Ord, Calif.).

CDEF—Committee on the Development of Engineering Faculties (American Society for Engineering Education).

CDF—Combat Defense Force. Cumulative frequency distribution.

CDO—Combat development office. Community dial office.

CDP—Checkout data processor (used on the BMEWS system). Communication data processor. Compound diffraction projector.

CDPC—Central data processing computer.

CDR—Controlled dynamic range.

CDRB—Canadian Defense Research Board.

CDRC—Conductivity-recording controller.

CDSE—Computer-driven simulation environment.

CDT—Canadian Department of Transport (Canadian equivalent of the FCC). Combined double tee. Control data terminal. Coordinate data transmitter (used in the SAGE system). Countdown time.

CDU—Coast defense unit.

CDX—Control differential synchro.

CE—Celestial equator. Chief engineer. Common emitter. Comparing element. Construction electrician's mate (U.S. Navy). Corps of Engineers.

C-E—Combined energy. Communications-electronics.

CEA—Cambridge electron accelerator. Canadian Electrical Association. Commissariat a l'Energie Atomique (French agency).

CEAC—Consulting Engineers' Association of California.

CEAO—Consulting Engineers' Association of Oregon.

CEASD—Consulting Engineers' Association of South Dakota.

CEAW—Consulting Engineers' Association of Washingotn.

CEB—Comite Electrotechnique Belge (Belgium).

CEBMCO—Corps of Engineers Ballistic Missile Construction Office.

CEC—Canadian Electrical Code. Consulting Engineers' Council.

CECIL—Compact electronic components inspection lab (developed by Spacionics Inc., Geneva, Ill.).

CECMRL—Communications - electronics consolidated mobilization reserve list.

CECS—Communications - electronics coordinating section.

CED—Communications - electronics doctrine (U. S. Air Force terminology).

CEDAC—Central differential analyzer control. Cooling effect detection and control.

CEE—Combat emplacement excavator. International Commission on Rules for the Approach of Electrical Equipment.

CEF—Carrier elimination filter. Complementary emitter follower.

CEGB—Central Electricity Generating Board (British agency).

CEI—Comitato Elettrotechnico Italiano (Italian organization). Communications - electronics instructions.

CEIP—Communications - electronics implementation plan.

CEL—Celestial. Combat elevation launches. Critical experiment laboratory.

CEM—Circular electric mode. Counter-electromotive.

CEMA—Canadian Electrical Manufacturers' Association. Communications Equipment Manufacturers' Association.

CEMS—Central electronic management system.

CENCATS—Central Pacific Combat Air Transport.

CENRAT—Central range timing station.

CENTO—Central Treaty Organization (successor to Baghdad Pact).

CEO—Communications - electronics officer. Consulting Engineers of Ohio.

CEP—Circular error probability.

CEPT—European Post and Telecommunications Conference.

CERAMETERM — Ceramic - metal terminal (developed by Bendix Aviation Corp.).

CERMA—Centre d'Etudes et de Recherches de Medicine Aeronautique (Air Research Medical Center—France).

CERN—European Organization for Nuclear Research.

35

CES—Candelabra Edison screw. Cleveland Engineering Society. Completely even-sided.

CESI—Closed entry socket insulator (developed by Cannon Electric).

CESO-W—Council of Engineers and Scientists Organizations—West.

CESR—Canadian Electronic Sales Representatives.

CETEX—Committee on Contamination by Extraterrestrial Exploration.

CEV—Combat engineer vehicle.

CEVM—Consumable electrode vacuum melting.

CEW—Copi - Elgot - Wright (logic nets).

CEWA—Canadian Electronic Wholesalers' Association.

CF—Carrier frequency. Central file. Change frequency. Circuit finder (teletype term). Conversion factor. Cotton-covered, heat-resistant fixture wire. Count forward.

CFA—Cleared for approach (CAA term). Crossed-field amplifier.

CFAR—Constant false alarm rate.

CFC—Crossed-film cryotron.

CFE—Contractor - furnished equipment.

CFF—Critical fusion frequencies.

CFM—Cubic feet per minute.

CFP—Change flight plan.

CFPD—Cotton-covered, heat-resistant cord.

CFPO—Cotton-covered, heat-resistant cord.

CFR—Catastrophic failure rate. Cumulative failure rate.

CFS—Center frequency stabilization. Central Flying School (Royal Air Force). Cubic feet per second.

CFT—Cotton, fabric tape. 100 feet.

CG—Captain of the Guard. Center of gravity. Central control. Clutter gate. Coast Guard. Commanding General. RF cable or transmission line (JAN nomenclature).

cg—Centigram.

CGAS—Coast Guard Air Station.

CGB—Convert gray to binary.

CGFP—Calcined gross fission products.

CGL—Center of gravity locator.

CGMO—Coast and Geodetic Magnetic Observatory.

CGN—Cruiser, guided - missile, nuclear.

CGOPHEOSE—Consultative group on potentially harmful effects of space experiments.

CGRE—Gas-cooled reactor experiment.

CGS—Coast and Geodetic Survey.

CGSC—Command and General Staff College.

CGTS—Coast and Geodetic Tide Station.

CH—Choke.

CHAL—Challenge.

CHALICE—Compressional Heating and Linear Injection Cusp Experiment (Stevens Institute of Technology).

CHARM—CAA high - altitude remote monitors.

CHG—Change.

CHIEF—Controlled handling of internal executive functions (UNIVAC computer program).

CHINFO—Chief of Naval Information.

CHLORO—Chloroprene.

CHNL—Channel.

CHQ—Corps headquarters.

c-hr—Candle-hour.

CHRG—Charge.

CI—Call indicator. Cast iron. Characteristic impedance. Circuit interrupter (JIC and NMTBA term). Cirrus (meteorological term). Concentrator - identifier. Cut in.

Ci—Curie.

C/I—Carrier-to-interference ratio.

CIA—Central Intelligence Agency.

CIB—Central Intelligence Board. Concrete Industry Board.

CIC—Combat Information Center. Cooperative Interference Committee. Counter-Intelligence Corps.

CICF—Chambre des Ingenieurs-Conseils de France.

CIE—Commission Internationale d'Eclairage (**International Commission** on Illumination—previously ICI).

CIF—Carriage, insurance and freight. Central index file (Dept. of Defense). Central Integration Facility.

CIFAX—Enciphered facsimile communications.

CIFP—Cancel instrument flight plan (CAA term).

CIFR—Cancel instrument flight rule clearance (CAA term).

CIG—Ceiling (CAA term). Comité International de Geophysique (International **Geophysical Committee**).

CIGRE—Conference Internationale des Grand Reseaux Electriques (International Conference on Large Electric Systems).

CIGTF—Central Inertial Guidance Test Facility (U. S. Air Force, Holloman Air Force Base).

CIM—Crystal impedance meters.

CIN—Communication-identification-navigation.

CINCAF—Commander - in - Chief, Asiatic Fleet.

CINC-NORAD—Commander - in - Chief, North American Air Defense.

CINCPAC—Commander - in - Chief, Pacific.

CINPOA—Commander - in - Chief, Pacific Ocean Areas.

CINS—Cryogenic inertial navigating system.

CIO—Combat intelligence officer.

CIP—Clean-in-place.

CIR—Circuit.

CIRVIS—Communications instructions for worldwide reporting of vital intelligence sighting from aircraft.

CIS—Corrosion-intercepting sleeve.

CISPR—International Special Committee on Radio Interference.

CIT—Call-in time.

CITE—Council of the Institute of Telecommunication Engineers.

CITEL—Inter-American Telecommunications Commission.

CIU—Chief, Intelligence Unit.

CJS—Canadian Joint Staff.

CJTF—Commander Joint Task Force.

CK — Check. Crystal kit (**JAN** nomenclature).

CKO—Checking operator (telephone term).

CKT—Circuit.

CL—Central line. Clamp (**JIC** term). Class. Closing station. Conversion loss. Course line. Light cruiser (U. S. Navy).

cl—Centiliter.

CLA—Clamp (NMTBA term). Clear and add.

CLASS—Computer-based laboratory for automated school systems (developed by Systems Development Corp.).

CLASSMATE—Computer language to aid and stimulate scientific, mathematical and technical education (developed by Rensselaer Polytechnic Institute).

CLD—Called line.

CLEAR—Complier, executive program, assembler routines (automatic programming system for Honeywell 290 computer).

CLG—Calling line.

CLGN—Cruiser, light, guided-missile, nuclear (U. S. Navy).

CLIP—Compiler and lan- 　**[Cont.]**

guage for information processing.

CLK—Hunter-killer cruiser (U. S. Navy).

CLKWZ—Clockwise.

CLN—Negative clipper.

CLP—Cross - linked - polyethylene. Positive clipper.

CLR—Clear. Combined line recording (telephone term). Computer language recorder.

CLT—Computer language translator.

CLU—Central logic unit. Circuit lineup.

CLVP—Craft, landing, vehicle-personnel.

C-L-X—Continuous lightweight exterior (sheathed cable).

CLZ—Close.

CM—Chrom-moly. Circular mil. Comparator (JAN nomenclature). Computer module. Minelayer (U. S. Navy).

CMA—Canadian Manufacturers' Association. Circular mil area.

CMC—Control-magnetization curve.

CMCT—Communicate.

CMDO—Consolidated material distribution objectives.

CMDR—Commander.

CMF—Circular mil foot. Coherent memory filter.

CMI—International Maritime Committee.

CML—Current mode logic.

CMLC—Civilian - Military Liaison Committee.

CMP—Computational. Controlled materials plan. Corps of Military Police.

CMPLX—Complex.

CMR—Common mode rejection. Communications moon relay (U. S. Navy project). Contract Management Region (U. S. Air Force).

CMRU—Committee on Manufacturers' Radio Use (National Association of Manufacturers).

CMSCI—Council of Mechanical Specialties Contractors Institute.

CMSN—Commission.

CMTI—Celestial moving-target indicator.

CMV—Common-mode voltage.

CN—Compensator (JAN nomenclature).

C/N—Carrier-to-noise.

CNCT—Connect.

CND—Condition.

CNES—National Center for Space Research (French agency).

CNET—Centre National d'Etudes des Telecommunications (National Telecommunications Center—French agency).

CNF—Conjunctive normal formula.

CNI—Committee for Nuclear Information. Communication-navigation - identification (U. S. Navy term).

CNL—Circuit net loss.

CNO—Chief of Naval Operations.

CNR—Carrier-to-noise power ratio.

CNRS—Centre National de la Recherche Scientifique (French agency).

CNT—Canadian National Telegraph. Counter.

CNTP—Committee for A National Trade Policy, (1025 Connecticut Ave. N.W., Washington 6, D.C.).

CNTR—Center.

CNTRL—Central.

CO—Changeover. Close-open. Complement. Crystal oscillator. Cutoff. Station open to official correspondence exclusively (International Telecommunications Union designation).

COAX—Coaxial. Coaxial cable.

COBI—Coded biphase.

COBOL—Common business-oriented language (computer term).

COBRID—Coaxial hybrid.

COC—Combat operations center.

CODAG—Combined diesel and gas

turbine.

CODAN—Carrier - operated device, antinoise.

CODASYL—Committee for Data Systems Languages.

CODES—Commutating detection system (infrared receiver developed by Air Force Cambridge Research Center).

CODIC—Computer - directed communications.

CODIPHASE—Coherent digital phased array system (developed by Sylvania).

CODIT—Computer direct to telegraph (RCA automatic data-transmission system at the Atlantic Missile Range.)

COE—Central office equipment (telephone term).

COED—Computer - operated electronic display (simulator developed by Bendix Systems Division —Ann Arbor, Mich.).

COEF—Coefficient.

COESA—U. S. Committee on Extension to the Standard Atmosphere.

COFEC—Cause of failure, effect and corrective action.

COFI—Confidential.

CofS—Chief-of-Staff.

COGB—Certified Official Government Business.

COGO—Coordinate geometry (civil engineering computer programming system developed by MIT).

COGS—Continuous orbital guidance system (developed by General Electric Co., Utica, N. Y.).

COHO—Coherent oscillator.

COIN—Counter-insurgency.

COLIDAR—Coherent light detection and ranging (laser device developed by Hughes Aircraft Co.).

COLRAD—College on Research and Development (Institute of Management Sciences).

COMAC—Continuous multiple - access comparator.

COMAR—Computer, aerial reconnaissance.

COMASWFORPAC — Commander Antisubmarine Warfare Force, Pacific Fleet (Ford Island, Pearl Harbor, Honolulu, Hawaii).

COMDT—Commandant.

COMEX—Combat expendable.

COMIC—Colorant mixer computer.

COMINCH—Commander-in-Chief (U. S. Fleet).

COMINT—Communications intelligence.

COMLO—Compass locator.

COMLOGNET—Combat logistics communication network.

COMM—Communication.

COMMCEN—Communications center.

COMMSWITCH—Communications failure - detecting and switching equipment (developed by Kellogg Switchboard for Atlas launching).

COMM Z—Communications zone.

COM / OPS / RAC—Communications, operational practices, and rules of the air committee.

COMOPTEVFOR—Commander Operational Test and Evaluation Force (U. S. Naval Base, Norfolk 11, Va.).

COMPAC—Computer program for automatic control.

COMPACT—Compatible algebraic compiler and translator (automatic program unit for the REP-4000 computer — General Precision).

COMPOOL—Communications pool.

Com Sat—Communications satellite.

COMSEC—Communications security.

COMSND—Commissioned.

COMSOC—Communications Spacecraft Operations Center **[Cont.]**

(NASA, Goddard Spaceflight Center, Greenbelt, Md.).

COMSOPAC—Commander South Pacific (U. S. Fleet).

COMTRAN—Commercial translator (computer term).

CONAC—Continental Air Command.

CONAD—Continental Air Defense.

CONALOG—Contact analog (Navy submarine piloting system).

CONARC—Continental Army Command.

CONC—Concentrated.

CONELRAD—Control of electromagnetic radiation.

CONGRESS—Contiguous node group restoral supervision and switching (developed by ITT).

CO-NO—Current operator - next operator.

CONST—Constant.

CONSTR—Construction.

CONT—Continue. Continuous. Control.

CONTRANS—Conceptual thought, random-net simulation.

CONUS—Continental United States.

COORS — Communications outage restoration section (U. S. Air Defense Command Facility).

COP—Coefficient of performance (thermoelectric term). Computer optimization package (developed by Honeywell).

COPERS—European Preparatory Commission for Space Research.

COPO—Copolene.

COR—Carrier-operated relay. Communications operations report.

CORA—Coherent antenna array.

CORAL—Correlated radio link (developed by Martin).

CORAS—Corridor assignment (CAA term).

CORC—Cornell computing language (compiler language developed by Cornell University).

CORDAT—Coordinate data set (developed by Burroughs Research Center, Paoli, Pa.).

CORDIC—Coordinate rotation digital computer (developed by General Dynamics, Fort Worth, Tex.).

CORG—Combat Operations Research Group (Fort Monroe, Va.).

COS—Completely odd-sided.

COSAL—Coordinated ships' allowance list.

COSAR—Compression scanning array radar (developed by Raytheon).

COSC—Canadian Chiefs - of - Staff Committee.

COSMON—Component open/short monitor (developed by Librascope, Glendale, Calif.).

COSOS—Conference on Self-Operating Systems.

COSPAR—Committee on Space Research of the International Council of Scientific Unions.

COST—Coordination of spindle-type tooling.

COSWA — Conferences on Science and World Affairs.

COTAR—Correlated orientation tracking and range system. Cosine-trajectory angle and range (developed by Cubic Corp.).

COZI—Communications zone indicator (developed by Raytheon).

CP—Candle power. Check parity. Check point. Check protection. Chicago pile. Clock phase. Clock pulse. Command post. Computer (JAN nomenclature). Construction permit. Control panel. Control point. Coupling/coaxial or waveguide junction. Creative power.

C-P—Cartesian to polar.

CPA—Closest point of approach. Color phase alternation. Critical path analysis.

CPAWS—Computer - planner and

aircraft weighing scales (built for U.S. Air Force by Baldwin-Lima-Hamilton Corp.).

CPC—Card-programmed calculator. Ceramic - wafer printed circuit. Computer process control. Cotton-covered, heat-resistant cord.

CPD—Combat potential display. Contact potential difference.

CPDA—Copper Products Development Association.

CPDD—Command post digital display.

CPE—Central programmer and evaluator.

CPEQ—Corporation of Professional Engineers of Quebec (Canadian organization).

CPEx—Command post exercise.

CPFF—Cost-plus-fixed-fee.

CPI—Crash position indicator.

CPIF—Cost-plus-incentive-fee.

CPIP—Computer pneumatic input panel.

CPM—Counts per minute. Critical path method.

CPO—Changing path of operation. Chief petty officer. Code practice oscillator. Controlled precision oscillator.

CPR—Cam plate readout.

CPRB—Combined Production and Resources Board.

CPS—Central processing system (computer term).

CPSO—Cumberland Plateau Seismological Observatory (McMinnville, Tenn.).

CPU—Central processing unit.

CPY—Copy.

CQ—General call.

CQI & R—Central qualifications inventory and referral system.

CQT—Correct.

CR—Call request (telephone term). Carriage return. Citizens radio. Command register. Control relay (JIC and NMTBA term). Con-

trolled rectifier. Count reverse. Crystal. Crystal detector. Crystal or metallic rectifier. Station open to limited public correspondence (ITU designation). Varistor.

CRA—Control relay automatic (JIC term). Cosmic-ray altimeter.

CRAF—Civil Reserve Aircraft Fleet.

CRAM—Card random access memory (National Cash Register Co. system).

CRBR—Controlled recirculation boiling reactor.

CRC—Carriage return contact. Circle. Consistency-recording controller. Control and reporting center.

CRCHF—Crew chief.

CRCM—Continuous-reading meter-relay.

CRD—Capacitor-resistor diode network.

CRE—Control relay electronically energized (JIC term).

CREA—Committee on the Relation of Electricity to Agriculture.

CRES—Corrosion-resistant.

CRF—Carrier-frequency telephone repeater. Control relay forward.

CRH—Control relay, hand (JIC term).

CRHS—Component reliability history survey.

CRI—Committee for Reciprocity Information.

CRIG—Capacitor rate - integrating gyro.

CRIS—Command retrieval information system (developed by Information Retrieval Corp.).

CRL—Control relay latch (JIC term).

CRM—Control relay master (JIC term).

CRMA—Commercial Refrigerator Manufacturers' Association.

CRMR—Continuous-reading meter-relay.

CROO—Citizens Radio   [Cont.]

Operators' Organization.

CROSS—Computer rearrangement of subject specialties.

CRP—Clausen rolling platform (British missile platform). Control and reporting post.

CRPL—Central Radio Propagation Laboratory (National Bureau of Standards, Boulder, Colo.).

CRREL—Cold Regions Research and Engineering Laboratory (U.S. Army laboratory, Wilmette, Ill.).

CRS—Citizens Radio Service. Cold rolled steel. Course.

CRTA—Chicago Radio Traffic Association.

CRTOG—Cartography.

CRTPB—Canadian Radio Technical Planning Board (200 St. Clair Ave., Toronto, Canada).

CRTPC—Canadian Radio Technical Planning Committee.

CRTS—Controllable radar target simulator.

CRTU—Combined receiving and transmitting unit (teletype term).

CRTV—Composite reentry test vehicle.

CRU—Combined rotating unit (employed in the Snap 2 power conversion). Control-relay unlatch (JIC term).

CRWO—Crypto room watch officer (U.S. Navy).

CRYPTO—Cryptography, cryptographic.

CRYPTONET — Crypto-communication network.

CRYST—Crystalline, crystals.

CRZ—Cruise.

CS—Carbon steel. Check sorter. Cirrostratus (meteorological term). Component percentage setter. Component scalar. Continental scatter. Control set (telephone term). Control signal. Controlled switch. Counting switch. Cumulative sum (quality-control term).

Cycles shift.

CSA—Canadian Standards Association. Communications service authorization.

CSAGI—Comité Special de l'Année Geophysique Internationale (International Geophysical Year).

CSAR—Communication satellite advanced research.

CSC—Central Simulation Council. Consequence counter.

CSD—Constant-speed drives.

CSE—Control systems engineering.

CSEA—California State Electronics Association.

CSH—Consequence history.

CSI—Construction Specifications Institute.

CSigO—Chief Signal Officer.

CSIRO — Commonwealth Scientific and Industrial Research Organization (Highett, Victoria, Australia).

CSM—Coffin strategic missile.

CSO—Chief Signal Officer.

CSP—Continuous stratification profiler. Control switching point (telephone term). Controlled surface process.

CSPE—Connecticut Society of Professional Engineers.

CSPO—Communications Satellite Project Office (Defense Communications Agency).

CSR—Clamped speed regulator (manufactured by Instrument Development Labs, Inc., Attleboro, Mass.).

CSRA—Chicago Suburban Radio Association.

CSSB—Compatible single-sideband.

CSSO—Consolidated Surplus Sales Office (Dayton Air Force Depot).

CSSR—Consolidated stock status report.

CST—Central Standard Time. Continuously stirred tank.

CSTR—Continuously stirred tank

reactor.

CSV—Corona starting voltage.

CT—Center tap. Coastal telegraph station; carrier telephone channel (ITU designations). Communication trench. Communications Technician (U.S. Navy). Constant temperature. Control transformer. Count. Counter. Counter tube. Current transformer.

CTA—Call Time Adjustor. Control area. Council for Technological Advancement.

CTAP—Contact approach (CAA term).

CTB—Commercial traffic bulletin.

CTC—Cam timing contact. Centralized traffic control. Contact.

CTCA—Channel and Traffic Control Agency.

CTCC—Change to, or contact center control (CAA term).

CTCF—Channel and technical control facility (used in U.S. Air Force Stratcom system).

CTCU—Channel and traffic control unit.

CTDS—Code-translation data system (developed by Hallicrafters for the U.S. Navy).

CTE—Coefficient of thermal expansion.

CTF—Change to tower frequency. Chlorine trifluoride (rocket fuel oxidizer). Common test facility (Ft. Huachuca, Ariz.). Core test facility.

CTFE — Chlorotrifluoroethylene (fluorocarbon plastic used as an insulator).

CTL—Confidence training launches. Control. Core-transistor-logic.

CTLI — Confidence-training-launching-instrumentation.

CTMA—Cutting Tool Manufacturers' Association.

CT(N)—Counter, n stages.

CTO—Central Treaty Organization.

C to F—Center to face.

CTP—Central transfer point.

CTR—Cavitation tendency ratio. Corrected average temperature rise.

CTS—Communications and tracking subsystems. Contract technical services.

CTT—Central trunk terminals.

CTU—Centigrade thermal unit.

CTUNA—Commercial Telegraphers' Union of North America.

CTV—Constant tangential velocity.

CTZ—Control zone.

CU—Coefficient of utilization (lighting term). Consumers' Union. Control unit. Coupling device (JAN nomenclature). Crystal unit (Piezoelectric).

CUE—Cooperating Users' Exchange (Computer users' organization).

CUG—Common user group.

CUL—See you later.

CUR—Current.

CURAGI—Comité pour l'Utilisation des Résultats de l'Année Geophysique Internationale (IGY Completion Committee).

CV—Aircraft carrier (U.S. Navy). Combined glass and cotton braid, lacquered. Common version. Continuously variable (refers to oscillators). Continuous vulcanization (used in curing wire insulation). Converter (JAN nomenclature). Counter voltage (JIC and NM-TBA term). Station open exclusively to the correspondence of a private agency (ITU designation).

CVA—Aircraft carrier (U.S. Navy).

CVAN—Aircraft carrier, attack, nuclear.

CVE—Aircraft carrier escort (U.S. Navy). Continuously variable, for emergency use (refers to oscillators).

CVM — Consumable vacuum melting.

CVMAS—Continuously variable mechanical-advantage shifter.

CVR—Carrier vessel reactor. Constant voltage reference. Controlled visual rules.

CVTR—Carolinas-Virginia pressure tube reactor.

CVU—Constant voltage unit.

CW—Calls waiting. Chemical warfare. Clockwise. Continuous wave. Copperweld conductor.

CWA—Communications Workers of America (Union — 1808 Adams Mill Rd., Washington, D.C.).

CWIF—Continuous-wave intermediate-frequency (Doppler system).

CWL—Chemical Warfare Laboratories (U.S. Army, Edgewood, Md.).

CWO—Chief Warrant Officer. Communication Watch Officer (U.S. Navy). Continuous-wave oscillator.

CWS—Chemical Warfare Service.

CWSD—Continuous-wave space duplexed (Doppler system).

CWT—Hundredweight.

CWV—Continuous-wave video. (Doppler system).

CX—Central exchange. Composite (telephone signaling system). Control transmitter. Cord (JAN nomenclature).

CY—Case (JAN nomenclature). Copy.

CYBORG—Cybernetic organism.

CYL—Cylinder.

D

D—Dacron. Debye. Density. Destroyer. Detectivity. Digit. Digital. Diode. Directivity. Directivity factor. Disaster. Display. Down (JIC and NMTBA term). Drag. Drum. Dynamotor. Electric displacement or electric flux density. Odd number.

d—Deci- (prefix—0.1 or 10^{-1}).

DA—Data available. Decimal add. Define area. Department of the Army. Detector amplifier. Discrete address. Distribution amplifier. Documents of acceptance. Dummy antenna (JAN nomenclature).

D-A — Deacon - Arrow (sounding rocket).

DAC—Digital arithmetic center. Digital-to-analog converter.

DACCC—Defense area communications control center.

DACI—Direct adjacent-channel interference.

DACOM—Datascope computer-output microfilmer (high-speed recording system developed by Eastman Kodak Co.).

DACOWITS—Defense advisory committee on women in the services.

DADEE—Dynamic analog differential equation equalizer (developed by Rocketdyne).

DADIT—Daystrom analog-to-digital integrating translator (developed by Daystrom Systems, LaJolla, Calif.).

DAE—District Airport Engineer.

DAEMON—Data adaptive evaluator and monitor (developed by American Bosch Arma Corp., Garden City, N.Y.).

DAF—Dansk Astronautisk Forening (Danish Astronautical Society). Department of the Air Force.

DAFD—Dayton Air Force Depot (Dayton, Ohio).

DAFSC—Duty Air Force specialty

code.

DAFT — Digital/analog function table (function generator manufactured by Packard Bell).

DAG—Deutsche Astronautische Gesellschaft (German).

DAGC—Delayed automatic gain control.

DAI—Drift angle indicator.

DAISY—Data acquisition and interpretation system (developed by Convair).

DAJS—Distributed area jamming system.

DAL—Directional arm lock.

DALC—Divided access line circuit (telephone term). Dynamic asynchronous logic circuit.

DALTO—Doman-approach-landing-takeoff.

DAM—Data-addressed memory.

DAMP—Downrange antimissile program (Army project operated by RCA).

DAMS—Defensive antimissile system.

DAP—Diallyl phthalate (resin used in molding electrical components). Diffused alloy power (high-power, high-frequency transistor).

DARA—Deutsche Arbeitsgemeinschaft fur Rechen-Anlagen (German Computer Association).

DARC—Deutschen Amateur Radio Club.

DART—Data analysis recording tape. Data reduction translator.

DAS—Data acquisition system. Digital attenuator system. Director of Administration Services.

DASA—Defense Atomic Support Agency.

DASH—Drone antisubmarine gyrodyne (Drone-helicopter-borne dip sonar). Drone antisubmarine helicopter.

DASM—Directorate of Advanced Systems Management (Wright Air Development Division).

DASP—Directorate of Advanced Systems Planning (U.S. Air Force).

DaSpan—Data-spanning (RCA communications system for data processing centers).

DAST—Directorate of advanced systems technology.

DASTARD—Destroyer Antisubmarine transportable array detector.

DAT—Drone-assisted torpedo. Duration-adjusting type.

DATAC—Digital automatic tester and classifier (diode sorter developed by Sylvania).

DATDC—Data Analysis and Technique Development Center (Alexandria, Va.).

DATICO—Digital automatic tape intelligence checkout (developed by Northrop Corp.).

DATS—Dynamic accuracy test system (automatic checkout system developed by RCA).

DAVC—Delayed automatic volume control.

DB—Diffused base. Display buffer. Double-break (relay term). Dynamic braking contactor or relay (JIC and NMTBA term).

db—Decibel.

DBA—Daytime Broadcasters' Association.

dba—Decibels above reference noise adjusted (reference level is —85 dbm).

dbc—Decibels relative to the carrier.

DBCP—Double-bounce, circularly polarized (radar system developed by Martin).

DBD—Double-base diode.

dbk—Decibels referred to one kilowatt.

DBL—Detail billing number required (telephone term).

dbm—Decibels referred to 1 milliwatt.

DBPC—Ditertiary butyl paracresol (transformer oil inhibitor).

DBR—Disk, balls, and roller integrator.

dbRaP—Decibels above reference acoustical power (10^{-16} watts).

dbrn—Decibels above reference noise (reference noise power is taken at 1000 cps and as -90 dbm).

dbv—Decibels referred to one volt.

dbw—Decibels referred to one watt.

dbx—Decibels above reference coupling.

dbμ—Field strength in db below one watt per square meter.

DC—Data collection. Decade counter. Define constant. Deposited carbon. Digital comparator. Direction center. Directional coupler.

DCA—Defense Communications Agency (U.S. Dept. of Defense). Defense Communications Advisory Committee. Digital Computers Association. Direction center active. Double-conversion adapter.

DCAR—Discrepancy and corrective action report (Quality control term).

DCAS—Data collection and analysis system (Goddard Space Flight Center automatic data collection system). Deputy commander for aerospace systems (5800 Arbor Vitae St., Los Angeles 45, Calif. —Bldg. 4).

DCC—Development Control Center.

DCCC—Defense Communications Control Center.

DCCS—Defense Communications Control System.

DCDR—Direct cycle diphenyl reactor.

DCE—Director for Communications-Electronics (joint staffs).

DCFEM—Dynamic crossed fields, electric and magnetic. Dynamic crossed-field electron multiplier.

DCL—Dynamic load characteristic.

DCMA—Defense Contract Management Association.

DCN—Drawing change notice.

DCNO—Deputy Chief of Naval Operations.

DCOT—Distant central office transceivers.

DCR—Data conversion receiver. Decrease. Direct conversion reactor.

DCRS—Data collection and reduction system.

DCS—Defense communications system (Defense Communications Agency). Deputy Chief of Staff. Direction center standby. Director control system. Double channel simplex.

DCS-M—Deputy Chief of Staff for Materiel (U.S. Air Force).

DCSPE—District of Columbia Society of Professional Engineers.

DCS/R&T—Deputy Chief of Staff for Research and Technology.

DCS/S&L—Deputy Chief of Staff for System and Logistics.

DCT—Direct carbon transfer recording.

DCTL—Direct-coupled transistor logic.

DCU—Decade counting unit. Decimal counting unit. Digital counting unit.

DCUTL—Direct - coupled unipolar transistor logic.

DCW—Define constant with word mark.

DCX—Direct current experiment (Oak Ridge).

DD—Decimal divide. Destroyer (U.S. Navy). Digital display. Double dacron braid lacquered. Double diffused. Drum demand.

DDA—Digital differential analyzer.

DDAS—Digital data acquisition system.

DDC—Data distribution center. Digital data converter.

DDCE—Digital data conversion

equipment.

DDD—Direct distance dialing.

DDE—Destroyer escort (U.S. Navy).

DDG—Digital display generator. Guided-missile destroyer (U.S. Navy).

DDI—Depression deviation indicator.

DDM—Difference in depth of modulation. Double-diffused mesa.

DDP—Department of Defense Production (Canadian government organization). Digital data processor.

DDR—Decoy discrimination radar. Digital data receiver. Digital demand recorder. Radar picket ship (U.S. Navy).

DDRI—Design drafting reference information system.

DDRR—Directional discontinuity ring radiator (antenna developed by Northrop Corp.).

DDS—Direct dispatching service. Doppler detection station.

DDT—Digital data transceiver. Digital data transmitter.

DDU—Dual diversity unit.

DE—Decision element. Destroyer escort (U.S. Navy). Display ended.

D/E—Deputy for Engineering.

DEAL—Decision evaluation and logic.

DEC—Decimal. Direct energy conversion.

DECCA—British long-range navigational aid in the 70-130 kc band.

DECM—Defensive electronic countermeasures.

DECMSND—Decommissioned.

DECOMP—Decomposition mathematical programming system (computer programming system employing Dantzig & Wolfe principle).

DECR—Decrease.

DECTRA—British radionavigational aid similar to Decca.

DECUS—Digital Equipment Computer Users' Society.

DEE—Digital evaluation equipment (developed by RCA).

DEFRIV—Defense along river (a simulated map war game involving defensive operations along a river line under conditions of simulated atomic warfare).

DEFT—Dynamic error-free transmission (developed by General Electric).

DEG—Guided missile escort ship.

deg—degree.

DEI—Development engineering inspection.

DEL—Delay.

DELRAC—British 10-14 kc, 3000-mile radionavigational aid.

DELTA—Differential electronically locking test accessory.

DELTIC—Delay line time compression.

DEMATRON—Distributed emission magnetron amplifier (a forward-wave amplifier developed by Litton Industries).

DE-ME-DRIVE—Decoding memory driving.

DEML—Detached enlisted memo list.

DENS—Density.

DEP—Dense electronic population.

DEPI—Differential equations psuedo-code interpreter (computer routine developed at Jet Propulsion Labs, Institute of Technology, Pasadena, Calif.).

DERM—Delayed echo radar marker.

DES—Digital expansion system.

DESC—Defense electronics supply center (Dayton, Ohio).

DESK FAX—Desk-top facsimile (Western Union system).

DET—Detachment.

DETA—Diethylenetriamine **[Cont.]**

(rocket fuel).

DETAB—Decision tables.

DETAB-X—Decision tables, experimental.

DEUCE—Digital electronic universal calculating engine (built by English Electric Co.).

DEVR—Distortion-eliminating voltage regulator (manufactured by Curtiss-Wright).

DEW—Directed energy weapons. Distant early warning.

DEXAN—Digital experimental airborne navigator (developed by General Electric Co.—England).

DF—Degrees of freedom. Describing function. Direction finder.

Df—Friction drag.

D-F—Direct flow.

DFA—Drap Forging Associations.

DF/FME — Direction - finding/frequency-measuring equipment.

DFG—Diode function generator. Discrete frequency generator.

DFL—Development Loan Fund.

DFP—Deviant flight plan. Dipole flat plate antenna.

DFR—Degradation failure rate.

DFSTN—Direction-finding station.

DG—Differential generator. Diode gate. Double-groove. Grown diffused.

DGDP—Double-groove, double-petticoat.

DGMS—Division of General Medical Sciences (U.S. Dept. of Health, Education and Welfare).

DGNL—Diagonal.

DGSC—Defense General Supply Center (Richmond, Va.).

DH—Deadhead. Display hold (telephone term).

DHE—Data-handling equipment.

DHFA—Dominion High Fidelity Association (Canadian hi-fi manufacturers' association).

DHI—Directional horizon indicator.

DHOF—Two-conductor, heat- oil-,

and flame-resistant wire.

DI—Deviation indicator. Directivity index. Discomfort index (meteorological term). Doppler-inertial. Double injection.

DIA—Defense Intelligence Agency (Dept. of Defense).

DIAC—Defense Industry Advisory Council.

DIAD—Drum information assembler and dispatcher.

DIAN—Decca integrated airborne navigator (developed by Decca Navigator Co., Ltd., England).

DIANE—Digital integrated attack navigation equipment.

DICBM—Defense intercontinental ballistic missile.

DICE—Digital integrated circuit elements.

DICON—Digital communications through orbiting needles.

DID—Digital information display. Direct inward dialing. Division of isotope development.

DIDA—Dynamic instrumentation digital analyzer.

DIDAP—Digital data processor (designed and built by Radiation, Inc.).

DIDF—Dual-input describing function.

DIGICOM—Digital communication system.

DIL—Dilute.

DIM—Dynamic impedance measurement.

DIMAPA — Dimethylaminopropylamine (curing agent).

DIMPLE — Deuterium - moderated pile, low-energy (Harwell, England).

DIN—Deutsche Industrie Normen (West German Standards).

DIOB—Digital input-output buffer.

DIPEC—Defense Industrial Plant Equipment Center (Defense Supply Agency).

DIPS—Development information processing system.

DIR—Deparmtent of Industrial Research (division of Canadian Government's Defense Research Board). Disassembly and inspection report.

DISC—Disconnect switch (JIC and NMTBA term).

DISCOM—Digital selective communications (developed by General Electric Co. for the U.S. Air Force).

DIV—Divide/divider.

DIY—Do-it-yourself.

DJ—Deflection electrode. Diffused junction.

dk—Deka- (Prefix—10).

DKT—Dipotassium tartrate (Piezoelectric material).

DL—Dacron braid lacquered. Data link. Delay. Delay line. Destroyer leader (U.S. Navy). Diode logic. Disjunctively linear (logic nets). Distributed lab. Dynamic load characteristic. Dielectric loading factor.

DLG—Guided missile frigate or escort (U.S. Navy).

DLGN—Destroyer leader, guided missile, nuclear (U.S. Navy).

DLO—Division library only.

DM—Decamired (optical term for expressing color temperature). Decimal multiply. Detecting mechanism. Differentiating mechanism. Diffused mesa. Diversionary missile. Draftsman (U.S. Navy). Light minelayer (U.S. Navy). Magnetic drum module.

D/M—Demodulator-modulator.

DMC—Digital microcircuit.

DME—Distance - measuring equipment.

DME-COTAR — Distance-measuring equipment-correlation tracking and ranging system.

DMED—Digital message entry device.

DMET—Distance measuring equipment TACAN.

DMIC—Defense metals information center.

DMM—Digital multimeter.

DMP—Disarmed military personnel.

DMPI—Desired mean point of impact.

DMR—Defective - material report (Quality control term).

DMS—Defense materials system. Delta milliohm sensor. High-speed minesweeper (U.S. Navy).

DMSS—Data multiplex subsystem.

DMTR—Heavy-water materials-testing reactor (British reactor at Dounreay, Scotland).

DN—Decimal number system. Delayed neutron. Department of the Navy. Driven gear.

DNA—Desoxyribonucleic acid (a genetic substance used in radiation experiments).

DNCC—Defense National Communications Control Center.

DNCCC—Defense National Communications Control Center.

DND—Department of National Defense (Canadian Government Agency).

DNF—Disjunctive normal formula.

DNS—Doppler navigation system.

DO—Defense order. Deviating oscillator. Digital output. Duty Officer.

DOC—Data optimizing computer. Department of Commerce. Direct operating cost.

DOCGEN—Document generator.

DOD—Department of Defense. Diameter over the dielectric (telephone cable).

DODDAC—Department of Defense Damage-Assessment Center.

DOF—Degree of freedom.

DOFL—Diamond Ordnance Fuse Laboratories (U.S. Army installation, Washington, D.C.).

DO/IT—Digital output-input translator.

DOL—Detached officers list.

DOM—Digital ohmmeters. Domain.

DOO—Director, Office of Oceanography.

DOPLOC—Doppler location (satellite-detection system developed for U.S. Army by Technical Appliance Corp.).

DORAN—Doppler range (A combination of DOVAP and AZUSA).

DORF—Diamond Ordnance Radiation Facility.

DORIS—Direct order recording and invoicing system (developed by IT&T).

DOS—Directorate of operational requirements.

DOT—Department of Transport (Canadian agency that issues radio licenses—similar to FCC).

DOT&C—Department of Trade and Commerce (Canadian government bureau).

DOVAP—Doppler velocity and position.

DP—Data processing. Dial pulsing. Diaphragm. Differential pressure. Diffused planar. Digit present. Domestic public. Driving power.

D-PAT—Drum-programmed automatic tester (developed by Hughes Aircraft Co.).

DPC—Data processing center. Data processing central (solid-state digital computer developed by Librascope). Defense Plant Corporation.

DPCA—Displaced-phase-center antenna.

DPCS—Difference pressure control switch.

DPDT—Double-pole double-throw.

DPE—Data-processing equipment.

DPF—Dynamic pressure feedback.

DPG—Data processing group (A division of the Office Equipment Manufacturers' Institute). Digital pattern generator.

DPMA—Data Processing Management Association (Park Ridge, Ill.).

DPPA—Double-pumped parametric amplifier.

DPPH — Diphenylpicrylhydrazyl (a "scavenger" material used to measure the number of free radicals in irradiation).

DPR—Department performance rating. Depolymerized natural rubber. Dial pulse repeater (telephone term).

DPS—Data processing subsystem.

D&PS—Development and Proof Services (U.S. Army Ordnance, Aberdeen, Md.).

DPSK—Differentially coherent phase-shift-keying.

DPSS—Data processing subsystem.

DPST—Double-pole single-throw.

DQC—Dynamic quantity control.

DQM—Data quality monitors.

DR—Data recorder. Dead reckon. Digital resolver. Directive antenna with reflector (ITU Designation). Discrimination radar. Divided ringing (telephone term). Drift. Driver gear. Drum.

D/R—Direct or reverse.

DRA—Defense Reorganization Act. Digital recorder analyzer. Doppler radar.

DRAC—Distributed read address counter.

DRAI—Dead reckoning analog indicator.

DRB—Decade resolver bridge. Defense Research Board (Canadian Dept. of National Defense).

DRCPR—Differential reactive current projection relay.

DRD—Division of Reactor Development (Atomic Energy Commission).

DRDTO—Detection radar data takeoff (developed by Data Systems Operations Division of Sylvania Electric Products, Inc. for BMEWS).

DRET—Direct re-entry telecommunications. Direct re-entry telemetry.

DREWS—Direct-readout equatorial weather satellite.

DRF—Discharge ringing frequency.

DRI—Data reduction interpreter.

DRIFT—Diversity receiving instrumentation for telemetry (developed by Lockheed for Polaris missile).

DRL—Differential reinforcements of low rates.

DRM—Digital ratiometers.

DRO—Destructive readout.

DROMDI—Direct readout miss-distance indicator.

DROT—Delayed range on target.

DRT—Dead reckoning tracer. Decade ratio transformer. Diode recovery tester.

DRTE—Defense Research Telecommunications Establishment (Canadian government agency).

DRV—Data recovery vehicle.

DS—Dead space. Decimal subtract. Define symbol. Department of State. Depth sounder. Device selector. Dial system. Display-started. Drum switch (JIC term). Dynamic speaker. Miscellaneous illuminating or indicating device.

DSA—Defense Supply Agency. Define symbol address. Dial service A.

DSB—Decade synchro bridge. Defense Science Board (U.S. Dept. of Defense). Document Security Branch. Double-sideband.

DSBI—Deutsche Societaet Beratender Ingenieure (German joint enterprise of nine consulting engineering firms).

DSBSC—Double-sideband suppressed-carrier.

DSC—Difference signal control.

DSDT—Discrete space and discrete time.

DSE—Data-storage equipment. Directorate of Systems Engineering.

DSF—Design safety factor (reliability term).

DSGA—Double-conductor, shipboard general use, armored cable.

DSIF—Deep space instrumentation facility.

DSIR—Department of Scientific and Industrial Research (British Government Agency).

DSL—Deep scattering layer.

DSM—Directorate of Systems Management.

DSMG—Designated Systems Management Group.

DSN—Deep space network.

DSO—Defense system operator. District staff officer.

DSOTS—Demonstration site operational test series (Project Mercury).

DSP—Double silver-plated.

DSR—Delayed sound reinforcement. Digit storage relay. Digital stepping recorder. Distributed-state response. Dynamic sideband regulator.

DSS—Direct station selection (telephone term).

DSSA—Defense Space Support Agency.

DSU—Data synchronization unit. Device-switching unit (computer term).

D-SV—Dynamic self-verification.

DSW—Drum switch (NMTBA term).

DT—Data transmission. Dental technician (U.S. Navy). Detecting leads (JAN nomenclature). Digital technique.

D/T—Deputy for technology.

DTA—Differential thermal analysis. Distributing terminal   **[Cont.]**

assembly. Double tape armored (heavy - duty buried telephone cable).

DTAL—David Taylor Aerodynamics Laboratory (Washington, D.C.).

DTC—Decision threshold computer (developed by Page Communications for scatter stations).

DTF—Data transmission feature. Drone test facility (Ft. Huachuca to Yuma, Ariz).

DTG—Data-time group.

DTI—Distortion transmission impairment. Division of Technical Information (U.S. Atomic Energy Commission—Oak Ridge, Tenn.).

DTMB—David Taylor Model Basin (U.S. Navy installation at Carderock, Md.).

DTn—Double tinned.

DTO—Data takeoff (radar systems). Detailed test objectives. Dollar **trade-off** (operational **research** term).

DTP—Directory tape processor.

DTPA — Diethylenetriaminepentaacetic acid.

DTR—Daily transaction reporting. Digital telemetering register (developed by General Electric).

DTS—Data-transmission system. Digital telemetering system. Double-throw switch.

DTSC—Data transmission study group.

DTVM—Differential thermocouple voltmeter.

DTWX—Dial teletypewriter serv-

ice.

DU—Duty cycle.

DUKW—Amphibious motor vehicle.

DUNC—Deep underwater nuclear counting (developed by U.S. Naval Ordnance Lab.).

DUO—Datatron Users' Organization.

DUT—Diode under test.

DVFR—Defense visual flight rules.

DVL—Distance velocity lab.

DVM—Digital voltmeter.

DVOM—Digital volt-ohmmeter.

DVST—Direct-viewing storage tube.

DW—Data word buffer. Dead weight. Drop wire.

DWA—Double-wire armor (wire-cable designation).

DWAC—Distributed write address counter.

DWG—Drawing.

DW PNT—Dew point.

DX—Distance. Duplex. Duplex repeater (teletype designation). Reception of distant stations.

DXRA—DXplorers Radio Association.

DY—Dynamotor (**JAN nomenclature**).

DYANA—Dynamic **analyzer-pro**grammer.

dyn—Dyne.

DYSAC—Digital simulated analog computer.

DYSTAC—Dynamic memory and storage analog computer (manufactured by Computer Systems, Inc.).

DZ—Drop zone.

E

E—Early warning (Air Force mission designation). Element. Elevation angle. Elevator cable (rubber). Evanohm. Even number. Hoist assembly (JAN nomenclature). Miscellaneous electrical part. Modulus of elasticity. Voltage (EMF).

EA—Electroacoustic Engineers' Association (engineering union).

EAA—Engineer and Architects Association. Experimental Aircraft Association (9711 W. Forest Park Dr., Hales Corners, Wis.).

EAC—Engineer Amphibious Command.

EAD—Extended active duty (U.S. Army).

EADIZ—Entering air defense identification zone.

EAFB—Edwards Air Force Base.

EAG—Equipment advisory group.

EAGER—Electronic audit gager. (Developed for Ford by Performance Measurements Co.).

EAGLE—Elevation angle guidance landing equipment (developed by Airborne Instruments Lab.).

EAL—Electromagnetic amplifying lens.

EAM—Electronic accounting machine.

EAME—Europe-Africa-Middle East.

EAR—Electronic audio recognition (machine classification of underwater echoes developed by Polarad).

EARC—Extraordinary Administrative Radio Conference.

EAS—Extended area service (telephone term).

EASA—Electrical Apparatus Service Association (formerly National Industrial Service Assoc., 7730 Carondelet Ave., St. Louis 5, Mo.).

EASB—Electronic area support base.

EASTAF—Eastern Transport Air Force.

EASY—Efficient assembly system.

EAT—Expected approach time.

EAX—Electronic automatic exchange.

EBI—Equivalent background input.

EBIC — Electron-bombardment-induced conductivity.

EBICON — Electron-bombardment-induced conductivity.

EBOR—Experimental beryllium oxide reactor.

EBPA—Electron beam parametric amplifier.

EBR—Experimental breeder reactor (NRTS, Idaho).

EBU—European Broadcasting Union.

EBW—Exploding bridgewire system (ordnance safety device developed by Librascope Division, General Precision, Inc.).

EBWR—Experimental boiling-water reactor.

EC—Electrical conductivity. Engineering changes. Engineering Corps.

ECA—Economic Cooperation Administration. Enter control area.

ECAC—Electromagnetic Capability Analysis Center (U.S. Dept. of Defense). Electromagnetic Compatibility Analysis Center (U.S. Navy Experiment Station, Annapolis, Md.).

ECAP—Electric companies' advertising program.

ECC—Electrocardiocorder. European Coordinating Committee.

ECCANE—East Coast Conference on Aerospace and Navigational Electronics.

ECChart—Electrocardiocharter.

ECCM—Electronic counter-countermeasures.

ECDC—Electrochemical diffused collector.

ECG—Electrocardiogram. Electrocardiograph.

ECH—Echelon.

ECL—Equipment component list.

ECLA—Economic Commission for Latin America.

ECLO—Emitter-coupled logic operator.

ECM—Electrochemical ma- **[Cont.]**

chining. Electric countermeasures. European Common Market (West Germany, France, Italy, Belgium, Netherlands, Luxembourg).

ECMA—European Computer Manufacturers' Association (Geneva, Switzerland).

ECME—Electronic countermeasures equipment.

ECM/ELINT—Electronic countermeasures/electronic intelligence.

ECMP—Electronic countermeasures program.

ECMR—Eastern Contract Management Region (Olmstead AFB, Pa.).

ECN—Engineering change notice.

ECO—Electron-coupled oscillator. Electronic Central Office. Erecting cutout.

ECP—Electronic circuit protector (developed and manufactured by Mechanical Products, Inc.). Engineering change proposed.

ECPD—Engineers' Council for Professional Development.

ECPIP—Electric companies' public information program.

ECRC—Engineering College Research Council.

ECRDC—Electronic Component Research and Development Grant (Canadian government grants for basic development in electronic components).

ECS—Electrocardioscanner. Engine control system. Environmental control system. Environmental-control support. Etched Circuits Society.

ECSC—European Coal and Steel Community.

ECTL—Emitter-coupled transistor logic.

ED—Electrochemical diffused collector. Electrical differential. External device. Existence doubtful.

E-D—Expansion-deflection.

EDA—Electronic differential analyzer. Electronic digital analyzer.

EDAC—Electronic dive-angle control. Error detection and correction (developed by Western Union).

EDB—Elongated die bushing.

EDCOM—Editor and compiler.

EDCW—External device - control word.

EDD—Envelope delay distortion.

EDDY—Electronic defense (developed by ITT).

EDF—Electricité de France (French National Electricity Commission).

EDGE—Electronic data - gathering equipment.

EDHE—Experimental data-handling equipment.

EDI—Electron diffraction instrument.

EDIT—Error deletion by iterative transmission.

EDITAR—Electronic digital tracking and ranging unit (radar tracking system developed by Canoga Electronics Corp.).

EDM—Electrical discharge machining. Electrodischarge machine.

EDMS—Engineering data micro-reproduction system.

EDP—Electronic data processing.

EDPC—Electronic data - processing center.

EDPE—Electronic data - processing equipment.

EDPM—Electronic data - processing machine.

EDPS—Electronic data - processing system.

EDRI—Electronic Distributors' Research Institute.

EDSAC—Electronic delay-storage automatic computer (completed in 1949 at Cambridge University).

EDSD—Electronics Defense Systems Division (Air Force).

EDT—Ethylenediaminetartrate (synthetic piezoelectric crystal).

EDTA — Ethylenediaminetetraacetic acid (a chelating agent).

EDTR—Experimental, developmental, test and research.

EDU—Electronic display unit.

EDVAC—Electronic discrete variable automatic computer (developed by University of Pennsylvania).

EE—External environment (reliability term).

EEA—Electronic Engineering Association (British manufacturers' organization—11 Green St., London, W.1., England. Formed in 1944 under name Radio Communication Electronic Engineering Association).

EEB—Eastern Electricity Board (British electrical power agency).

EEC—European Economic Community.

EED—Electrically initiated explosive device.

EEE—Electrical engineering exposition.

EEG—Electroencephalogram. Electroencephalograph.

EEI—Edison Electric Institute. Environmental Equipment Institute. Essential elements of information.

EER—Envelope elimination and restoration. Explosive echo ranging.

EES—Engineering experiment station (U. S. Navy).

EET—Electrical equipment trailer. Explosive-to-electric transducer.

EETF—Electromagnetic environmental test facility (Fort Huachuca, Ariz.).

EF—Polyethylene tape. Emitter follower.

EFAS—Electronic flash approach system.

EFCR—Experimental fast ceramic reactor.

EFFBR—Enrico Fermi fast breeder reactor.

EFFI—Electronic fiber-fineness indicator. Electronic Forum for Industry. (British organization).

EFFORPA—Elliptic function first-order ripple-phase approximation.

EFM—Electric field meter. Expeditionary force messages.

EFPH—Equivalent full power hours.

EFSORPA—Elliptic function second-order ripple-phase approximation.

EFTA—European Free Trade Association (Britain, Norway, Sweden, Denmark, Austria, Switzerland, Portugal).

EFTO—Encrypt for transmission only.

EG—Environment generator. Executive generator (Philco 2000 computer term).

EGAD—Electronegative gas detector (developed by Westinghouse). Electronic ground automatic destruct sequencer.

EGAL—Elevation guidance for approach and landing.

EGCR—Experimental gas-cooled reactor.

EGMTR—Eglin Gulf missile test range. (U. S. Air Force range in Florida).

EGO—Eccentric orbiting geophysical observatory (satellite).

EGT—Exhaust gas temperature.

EGTR—Eglin Gulf test range.

EHD—Electrohydrodynamics.

EHF—Electrohydraulic forming. Extremely high frequency.

EHP—Effective horsepower.

EHV—Extra high voltage.

EIA—Electronic Industries Association.

EIAC—Electronic Industries Association of Canada.

EIC—Engineering information center. Engineering Institute of Canada.

EIMB—Electronics Installation and Maintenance Bulletin.

EIS—End interruption sequence.

EIT—Engineer-in-training.

EIV—Engine installation vehicle.

EJC—Engineers' Joint Council.

EJCC—Eastern Joint Computer Conference.

EKG—Electrocardiogram. Electrocardiograph.

EKS—Electrocardiogram simulator.

EKW—Electrical kilowatts.

EL—Electroluminescent. Elevation.

ELC—Extra-low carbon.

ELD—Edge-lighted display. Extralong distance.

ELDO—European Launcher Development Organization.

ELE—Electronic launching equipment (developed by ITT).

ELEKTRA—Radio navigation aid that provides a number of equisignal zones.

ELEM—Element.

ELF—Electroluminescent ferroelectric. Extremely low frequency.

ELInt—Electronic intelligence.

ELPE—Electroluminescent-photoelectric.

ELPG—Electric Light and Power Group.

ELSEC—Electronic security.

ELSIE—Electronic letter sorting and indicator equipment.

ELSSE—Electronic sky screen equipment.

ELT—Electrometer.

ELVIS—Electroluminescent vertical indication system (developed by Avien, Inc.).

EM—Efficiency modulation. Electrician's Mate (U. S. Navy). Electromagnetic. Electromechanical. Electro microscope. Epitaxial mesa. Exposure meter.

EMA—Electronic Manufacturers' Association, Inc. Electronic Missile Acquisition.

E-MAD—Engine maintenance, assembly and disassembly.

EMAR—Experimental memory-address register.

EMATS—Emergency message automatic transmission system.

EMC—Engineering Manpower Commission (29 W. 39th St., New York 18, N. Y.). Etched metal circuit.

EMCCC—European Military Communications Coordinating Committee.

EMCON—Emission control.

EMDI—Energy management display indicator.

EME—Electromagnetic environment (Ft. Huachuca, Ariz.)

EMEA—Electronic Maintenance Engineering Association (FAA Aeronautical Center, Oklahoma City, Okla.—society for Federal Aviation Agency engineers and technicians).

EMEB—East Midlands Electricity Board (British electrical power agency).

EMF—Electromotive force. Explosive metal forming.

EMG—Electromyograph.

EMI—Electromagnetic interference.

EMIS—Electromagnetic Intelligence System.

EMISS—Electromolecular instrument space simulator.

EML—Equipment modification list.

EMMA—Eye-movement measuring apparatus.

EMMCC—Erection mechanism motor control center (missile term).

EMO—Emergency Measures Organization (Canadian agency).

EMP—Electromechanical power.

EMPE-AERIS—Electronic mobile positioning equipment-aerial electronic range instrumentation system (developed by Cubic Corp.).

EMPIRE—Early manned planetary-interplanetary round trip experiment (Marshall Space Flight Center—study program). Electronic multipurpose intelligence retaliatory equipment.

EMR—Executive management responsibility.

EMS—Electronic management system. Electronic medical system. Emission spectrograph.

EMSA—Electron Microscope Society of America.

EMSL—Electronic Material Sciences Laboratory (Division of Air Force Cambridge Research Center).

EMT—Electrical mechanical tubing.

EMTI—Edge-mounted threaded inserts.

EMTTF—Equivalent mean time to failure.

ENCA—European Naval Communication Agency.

END—Earth-net dial.

ENEA—European Nuclear Energy Agency.

ENDOR—Electron-nuclear double resonance.

ENIAC—Electronic numerical integrator and computer (developed by University of Pennsylvania).

ENIC—Voltage negative-impedance converter.

ENIMS—Experimental scientific research institute for metal-cutting machine tools (Moscow, USSR).

ENSI—Equivalent - noise - sideband input.

EO—Elevator cable (rubber). Engineering order. Ethylene oxide. Executive Officer. Executive order. Ex officio.

EOAR—European Office of the Office of Aerospace Research (U. S. Air Force).

EOARDC—European Office Air Research and Development Command.

EOB—Electronic Order of Battle.

EOC—Electronics Operations Center. Error of closure. Experimentation Operations Center.

EOCR—Experimental organic-cooled reactor (NRTS, Idaho).

EODB—Explosive ordnance disposal bulletin.

EOE—Errors and omissions excepted.

EOF—Expected operations forecast.

EOL—End of life (reliability term).

EOLM—Electro - optic - light -modulator.

EOM—End of message.

EOQ—Economic order quantity.

EOR—Earth orbit rendezvous.

EOS—Electro-optical systems.

EOT—End of tape (computer tape term). End of transmission.

EOTS—Electro-optical tracking system (developed by American Optical Co.).

EP—Elongated punch. End of program. Epitaxial. Etched Plate. Extended play (45-RPM phonograph record). Extreme pressure.

E-P—Evaporation minus precipitation.

EPA—Electron probe analyzer. Ethyl ether, isopentane and ethanol. European Productivity Agency.

EPBX—Electronic private branch exchange.

EPC—Easy processing channel. Electronic program control.

EPCCS—Emergency positive control communications system. (Air Force communications system).

EPDC—Economic power dispatch computer.

EPDCC—Elementary potential digital computing component.

EPDS—Electronic Parts Distributors' Show.

EPEC—Emerson programmer-evaluator-controller (systems checkout equipment developed by Emerson Electric Co., St. Louis, Mo.).

EP & EM—Association of Electronic Parts and Equipment Manufacturers, Inc.

EPGCR—Experimental prototype gas-cooled reactor (Oak Ridge, Tenn.).

EPI—Earth path indicator (developed for Project Mercury by Minneapolis-Honeywell). Electronic position indicator. Expanded partial PPI indicator. Expanded position indicator.

EPMA—Electronic Parts Manufacturers' Association.

EPR—Electron paramagnetic resonance. Ethylene-propylene rubber (synthetic rubber). Exhaust pressure ratio.

EPRA—Electronic Production Resources Agency (U. S. Dept. of Defense).

EPSA—Electrostatic particle-size analyzer.

EPSL—Eastern Primary Standards Laboratory (Naval Gun Factory, Washington, D.C.).

EPT—Electrostatic printing tube. Ethylene-propylene-dicyclopentadiene terpolymer.

EPTA—Expanded Programme of Technical Assistance (United Nations).

EPU—Electrical power unit. European Payments Union.

EQ—Equalizer.

EQL—Expected Quality Level.

EQP—Equipment.

EQPMT—Equipment.

EQU—Equate.

ER—Echo ranging. Error relay.

E/R—Echo-to-reverberation.

ERA—Electrical Research Association (British organization). Electronic reading automation (a machine that reads printed characters, manufactured by Solartron, Surrey, England). Electronic Representatives Association. Electronic

Research Association (British electrical and allied industries).

ERC—Enlisted Reserve Corps.

ERD—Exponentially retrograded variable capacitance diode.

ERDA—Electronic Resources Development Agency.

ERDL—Engineering Research and Development Laboratories (Corps of Engineers, Fort Belvoir, Va.).

ERDR—Earth rate directional reference.

ERFA—European Radio Frequency Agency.

ERG—Electroretinogram.

ERIC—Electronic remote and independent control (Tractor-trailer guidance system using wire taped to floor).

ERMA—Electronic reading method of accounting. Electronic recording machines, accounting (developed by Stanford Research Institute, manufactured by General Electric Co.). Electronic recording method of accounting (data processing machine manufactured by General Electric).

ERNIE—Electronic random numbering and indicating equipment.

ERP—Effective radiated power.

ERPA—Electronic Production Resources Agency (U. S. Dept. of Defense).

ERR—Error.

ERSA—Electronic Research Supply Agency.

ERSER—Expanded reactance series resonator.

ERX—Electronic remote switching.

ES—Electrochemical Society. Electromagnetic storage. Executive secretary. External shield. Standard Edison screw.

ESA—Engineers and Scientists of America (federation of engineering unions).

ESAR—Electronically steerable array radar (developed by Radio Division, Bendix Corp.).

ESBC—Electronics Small Business Council (1000 Vermont Ave. N.W., Washington, D. C.).

ESC—Eastern Simulation Council. Electronics Systems Center (Air Materiel Command).

ESCAT—Canadian equivalent of U. S. Scater Plan for security control of civil aircraft and electromagnetic radiation.

ESD—Electronic Systems Division (U. S. AFSC). Elongated single domain (magnet term).

ESDA—Electronic Service Dealers' Association (mid-state, Pa.).

ESF—Even side flat.

ESFETA—Empire State Federation of Electronic Technicians' Associations (New York State).

ESG—Electrically suspended gyros. Electronic sweep generator. Electrostatically suspended gyroscope. Engineers' and Scientists' Guide (union of engineers and scientists).

ESLO—European Space Launcher Organization.

ESM—Edible structure material. Electromatic speed meter. Elektronisch Gesteuertes System mit Magnetfeld Kopplern (electronically controlled system with magnetic coupling developed by Siemens in Germany).

ESMA—Electronic Sales and Marketing Managers' Association.

ESO—Electronic Supply Office (U. S. Navy—Great Lakes, Ill.).

ESP—Electrosensitive programming.

ESPS—Engineering Societies Personnel Service.

ESR—Effective signal radiated. Electron spin resonance. Electronic scanning radar. Equivalent series resistance.

ESRD—Engineers and scientists engaged in research and/or development.

ESRO—European Space Research Organization.

ESS—Electronic switching system. Experimental SAGE sector.

ESSB—Electronic supply support base.

ESSEX—Experimental solid-state exchange (telephone term).

ESSFL—Electron steady-state Fermi level.

ESSL—Eastern Secondary Standards Laboratories (U. S. Naval Labs).

ESSPO—Electronic Supporting System Project Office (air research and development directorate at Wright-Patterson AFB).

ESSU—Electronic selective switching unit.

EST—Eastern Standard Time (mean time based on 75th Meridian west longitude). Estimate.

ESV—Earth satellite vehicle.

ET—Effective temperature. Electronic tube (JIC and NMTBA term). Electronics Technician (U. S. Navy). Elevator cable (thermoplastic). Ephemeris time.

ETA—Estimated time of arrival.

ETC—Electronic temperature control.

ETD—Estimated time of departure.

ETG—Electronics Technician Guild (Boston, Mass.).

ETI—Engine test information.

ETIM—Elapsed time.

ETL—Electronic Technology Lab (Wright Air Development Division). Electrotechnical laboratory (established and operated by Communications Ministry, Japanese Government). Etching by transmitted light.

ETO—Electronic temperature-offsetting signal.

ETP—Electrical tough pitch (type of copper used in con-   **[Cont.]**

ductors). Eleçtronic tape printer.

ETR—Engineering test reactor. Estimated time of return.

ETRC—Educational television and radio center. Engineering test reactor critical facility.

ETS—Electronic timing set. Engine test stand.

ETSAL—Electronic terms for space age language.

ETV—Educational television.

ETVM—Electrostatic transistorized voltmeter.

E-U—Engineer-user (missile flight analysis term).

EUCLID—Experimental use computer, London integrated display (British system of air traffic control).

EURATOM—European Atomic Energy Community.

EUREKA—Ground beacon of the British Rebecca-Eureka navigation system (220-kc band transponder).

EUSEC—Conference of Engineering Societies of Western Europe and the United States.

eV—Eingetragener Verein (German for "Registered Society"—similar to Inc.). Electron volt.

EVA—Electronic velocity analyzer.

EVATA—Electronic-visual-auditory training aid.

EVOP—Evolutionary operation.

EVT—Elasticity, viscosity and tixotropy (refers to rheological pro-

perties).

E/VTS—Engine and vehicle test stand.

EW—Early warning. East-west. Electronic warfare.

EWCL—Electromagnetic Warfare and Communications Laboratory (Wright-Patterson AFB).

EW/CRP—Early warning/control and reporting post.

EWD—Electronic Warfare Department.

EWFH—East-west fine, hundreds.

EWFT—East-west fine, tens.

EWFU—East-west fine, units.

EWO—Electronic Warfare Officer. Emergency War Operations.

EWP—Emergency war plan.

EWR—Early warning radar.

EWS—Early warning system.

EX—Execute. Exclusive or. Experimental. Experimental station (ITU designation). Extract.

EXC—Excitation.

EXCH—Exchange.

EXCLU—Exclusive.

EXCP—Except.

EXOS—Executive Office of the Secretary.

EXPRO—Office of Experimental Programs.

EXTRADOP—Extended-range DOVAP (RCA development).

EXTSN—Extension.

EZ—Electrical zero.

F

F—Fahrenheit. Farad. Feedback. Fermi. Filament. Filter (JAN nomenclature). Fixed. Forward (JIC and NMTBA term). Frigate. Fuse. Fused teflon.

FA—Aeronautical Station (ITU

designation). Fatty acid. Field accelerating contactor or relay (JIC and NMTBA term). Field artillery. Final address register. Fixed (Alaska). Frequency agility. Fused alloy.

FAA—Federal Aviation Agency.

FAB—Aeronautical broadcast station (ITU designation).

FABMIDS—Field army ballistic missile defense system.

FAC—Forward air controller. Frequency Allocation Committee (ITU).

FACD—Foreign area customer dialing.

FACI—First article configuration inspection (U. S. Air Force inspection).

FACOM—Long-distance measuring or radio navigation system using phase comparison technique at low frequency. Fuji Communication Apparatus Manufacturing Co., Ltd. computer (Japanese computer series).

FACT—Fairchild assured customer test. Flexible automatic circuit tester (developed by Hughes Aircraft Co.). Fully automatic compiling technique (developed by Datamatic Division, Minneapolis-Honeywell).

FAGC—Fast automatic gain control.

FAI—Federation Aeronautique Internationale.

FA I—Ferrite-Air I.

FA II—Ferrite-air II.

FAID—Flame ionization analyzer and detector.

FAP—Fortron Assembly Program.

FAQ—Fair average quality.

FAR—Failure analysis report.

FARADA—Failure-rate data exchange program.

FARET—Fast reactor experiment test (Argonne National Laboratory, Lemont, Ill.).

FARGO—Fourteen-o-one automatic-report-generating operation (IBM compiler system).

FAS—Flight assistance service.

FASRON—Field maintenance squadron (U. S. Navy Bureau of Aeronautics).

FAST—Facility for automatic sorting and testing (transistor test equipment manufactured by Texas Instruments). Fast automatic shuttle transfer. Federation of Scientific and Technical Associations (Italian organization). Fieldata applications, systems, and techniques. Flight advisory service test. Formula and statement translator (Honeywell compiler).

FAT—Factory acceptance test. Fast automatic transfer (machine for producing transistors at Lansdale Tube Division of Philco). Flight test station (ITU designation).

FATF—Free air test facility.

FAV—Fixed-angle variable delivery (hydraulic pump term).

FAWS—Flight Advisory Weather Service.

FAX—Aeronoutical fixed station (ITU designation). Facsimile.

FB—Base station (ITU designation). Fine business.

FBI—Federation of British Industries.

FBIS—Foreign Broadcast Intelligence Service.

FBM—Fleet ballistic missile.

FBMP—Fleet ballistic missile program.

FBMS—Fleet ballastic missile system.

FBMWS—Fleet ballistic missile weapon system.

FBPD—Foreign Business Practices Division (U. S. Dept. of Commerce).

FBR—Fast burst reactor.

FBW—Fly-by-wire.

FC—Coast station (ITU designation). Field camera. Filter center. Fire Controlman (U. S. Navy). Flight control.

fc—Foot-candle.

FCA—Federal Communica- **[Cont.]**

tions Act. Field-change authorization. French Computing Association. Frequency Control Analysis Center.

FC&A—Frequency control and analysis.

FCB—Marine broadcast station (ITU designation).

FCBA—Federal Communications Bar Association.

FCC—Face-centered cubic. Federal Communications Commission. Field camera control. Field control central. Fluid catalytic cracking.

FCCA—Forestry, Conservation Communications Association.

FCCN—Federal Communications Commission Network.

FCD—Frequency compression demodulator.

FCDA—Federal Civil Defense Administration.

FCDR—Failure cause data report.

FCDT—Four-coil differential transformer.

FCE—Fire control equipment. Frequency converter excitation.

FCE-SR—Frequency converter saturable reactor.

FCF—Frequency-compressive feedback.

FCI—Fluid Controls Institute.

FCL—Flight Control Laboratory (Wright-Patterson AFB).

FCM—Forged chrom-moly.

FCO—Functional checkout.

FCS—Fire control simulator. Fire control system. Flight control system. Forged carbon steel.

FCSF—Four - conductor, combination, special-purpose, flexible cable.

FCT—Filament center tap.

FCU—Flight control unit.

FCWG—Frequency control working group.

FD—Field-decelerating contractor or relay (JIC and NMTBA term).

Forced draft. Frame difference. Free delivery. Frequency diversity. Frequency divider. Frequency division.

F&D—Faced and drilled.

FDC—Fire Direction Center. Fluid digital computers.

FDDL—Frequency division data link.

FDI—Flight director indicator.

FDM—Frequency - division multiplex.

FDS—Frame difference signal.

FDTK—Floating drift tube klystron.

FE—Ferroelectric.

FEAF—Far East Air Forces.

FEB—Functional electronic block (molecular electronics term).

FEBS—Functional electronic blocks.

FE-EL—Ferroelectric - electroluminescent.

FEF—Fast extrusion furnace.

FE&MB—Field Engineering and Monitoring Bureau (division of the FCC).

FEMF—Foreign EMF (telephone term).

FEMITRON—Field emission microwave device.

FEN—Far East Network. (broadcasts from Japan).

FEP — Fluorinated ethylene propylene (Teflon 100, a fluorocarbon).

FES—Florida Engineering Society.

FET—Field-effect transistor.

FETF—Flight engine test facility.

FEVAC—Ferroelectric variable capacitor.

FEXT—Far-end crosstalk loss.

FF—Flexi-filamented. Full-field contractor or relay (JIC and NMTBA term). Rubber-covered fixture wire, flexible stranding.

F-F—Flip-flop.

FFAG—Fixed field alternating gradient.

FFAR—Folding fin aircraft rocket.

FFH—Heat-resistant, rubber-covered

fixture wire, flexible stranding.

FFI—Fuel flow indicator.

FFP—Firm fixed price.

FFRC—Flow-recording ratio controller.

FG—Flow gauge.

Fg—Forward gate.

FGD—Fine-grain data.

FHOF—Four-conductor, heat-, oil-, and flame-resistant wire.

fhp—Friction horsepower.

FI—Field intensity. Fighter-interceptor. Fixed interval. Flow indicator.

FIA—Flight information area.

FIAD—Flame ionization analyzer and detector (manufactured by Carad Corp., Palo Alto, Calif.).

FIANI—International Federation of National Associations of Engineers.

FIAT—Field Information Agency Technical (U. S. Army).

FIC—Flight Information Center. Frequency interference control.

FID—Federation Internationale de Documentation. Field Intelligence Department (U. S. Army).

FIDIC—International Federation of Consulting Engineers.

FIDO—Fallout intensity detector oscillator (developed by Controls for Radiation, Inc., Cambridge, Mass.).

FIER—Foundation for Instrumentation Education and Research.

FIFO—Floating input-floating output.

FIG—Figure.

FIL—Filament.

FILS—Flarescan instrument landing system.

FIM—Failure-indicating module. Field intensity meter. Flight information manual.

FIR—Far infrared. Flight information region. Food irradiation reactor. Full indicator reading.

FIRC—Forest Industries Radio Communications.

FIRETRAC—Firing error trajectory recorder and computer (developed by Aerojet-General's Ordnance Engineering Division).

FIS—Fighter-interceptor squadron.

FIT—Fabrication, integration, and test.

FJ—Fused junction.

FJCC—Fall Joint Computer Conference.

FL—Field-loss contactor or relay (JIC and NMTBA term). Filter. Flanged. Flight level. Float switch (JIC term). Foot-lambert. Land station (ITU designation).

FLAC—Florida Automatic Computer (U. S. Air Force Missile Test Center, Cocoa Beach, Fla.).

FLASH—Telephone procedure (NATO designation).

FLBIN—Floating-point binary.

FLCR—Fixed length cavity resonance.

FLD—Field.

FLDEC—Floating-point decimal.

FLE—Telemetering land station (ITU designation).

FLEA—Flux logic element array (developed by RCA).

FLF—Flip-flop.

FLFT—Full load frame time.

FLG—Flange.

FLGD—Flanged.

FLH—Hydrological and meteorological land station (ITU designation).

FLI—Flight leader identity.

FLIDAP—Flight data position.

FLIDEN—Flight data entry (developed by Aeronutronic Systems, Inc., division of Ford).

FLIP—Flim library instantaneous presentation (developed by Benson-Lehner). Flight launch infrared probe. Floating instrument platform.

FLOLS—Fresnel lens opti- **[Cont.]**

cal landing system.

FLS—Flow switch (JIC and NMTBA term).

FLSW—Fleet logistic support wing (U. S. Navy).

FLT—Filter. Flight.

FM—Feedback mechanism. Ferrite-metal. Field manual. Filament mid-tap. Frequency modulation.

FMA—Ferrite Manufacturers' Association.

FMAP—Fan marker approach.

FMB—FM Broadcasters.

FM-CW—Frequency modulation continuous wave.

FMD—Frequency of minimum delay.

FMDA—FM Development Association.

FME—Frequency-measuring equipment.

FMEVA—Floating point mean and variance (routine for computing mean and variance of a set of numbers on the Philco 2000 computer).

FMF—Fleet Marine Forces.

FMFB—Frequency modulation with feedback.

FMIC—Frequency monitoring and interference control.

FMKR—Fan marker.

FML—Front-mounting light.

FMQ—Frequency-modulated quartz.

FMR—Final meteorological radiation.

FMRT—Final meteorological radiation tape.

FMTS—Field maintenance test station.

FN—Furniture (JAN nomenclature).

FNIE—Federation Nationale des Industries Electroniques Francaises. (National Federation of French Electronics Manufacturers).

FNS—Functional signal nomenclature.

FO—Fan out. Field officer. Field order.

FOC—Flight Operations Center.

FOCOHANA—Fourier coefficient harmonic analyzer.

FOD—Foreign object damage.

FOI—Fighter officer for interceptors.

FOIF—Free oceanographic instrument float.

FOM—Fighter officer for missiles. Figure of merit.

FOPT—Fiber optic photo transfer.

FORDIO—Forecast of radio propagation conditions.

FORDS — Floating ocean research and development station.

FORTRAN—Formula translation.

FOSDIC—Film optical scanning device for input to computers (developed by National Bureau of Standards).

FOT—Optimum traffic frequency.

FP—Full period.

FPA—Fill Producers' Association. Flying Physicians' Association.

FPC—Federal Power Commission.

FPE—Fixed price with escalation.

FPI—Fuel pressure indicator.

FPIF—Firm target incentive contract.

FPIS—Forward propagation by ionospheric scatter. Successive target incentive contract.

FPL—Frequency phase lock (control system developed by Sequential Electronic Systems, Inc., Elmsford, N.Y.).

FPM—Feet per minute.

FPO—Fixed path of operation. Future projects office (NASA).

FPPS—Flight plan processing system (British system).

FPR-A—Prospective price redetermination at a stated time or times during performance.

FPR-C—Retroactive and prospective price redetermination at a stated time during performance.

FPRS—Forest Products Radio Service.

FPS—Field power supply. Fixed-point system.

FPTS—Forward propagation by tropospheric scatter.

FQI—Fuel-quantity indicator.

FR—Fixed ratio. Failure rate. Flow recorder. Frequency-measuring device (JAN nomenclature). Frequency response. Receiving station (ITU designation).

Fr—Franklin.

F$_r$—Flow ratio.

F-R—Fire-resistant.

FRA—Future Rocketeers of America (5075 Catalon Ave., Woodland Hills, Calif.).

FRAC—Fractionator reflux analog computer (developed by Phillips Petroleum Co., manufactured by Minneapolis-Honeywell).

FRAM—Fleet rehabilitaiton and modernization (Navy program).

FRC—Federal Radiation Council. Federal Radio Commission (now the Federal Communications Commission). Flight research center (NASA installation, Edwards Air Force Base, Calif.). Flow recorder-controller.

FRED—Fiendishly rapid electronic device. Figure-reading electronic device (character reader developed by EMI in England).

FREFAL—Floating point regula falsi (routine for computing roots on Philco 2000 computer).

FRENA—Frequency and amplitude (communications system developed by Philips Research Labs for high noise paths).

FRENAC—Frequency and amplitude coded.

FRESCANAR—Frequency scanning radar.

FRF—Flight readiness firing.

FRINGE—File and report information-processing generators (computer term).

FRO—Flight Radio Officer.

FROST—Food reserves on space trips.

FRP—Fiberglass-reinforced plastic.

FRT—Flow-recording transmitter.

FRTISO—Floating point root isolation.

FRTSAP—Federation of Radio and TV Service Associations of Pennsylvania.

FRUGAL—Fortran rules used as a general applications language.

FS—Floating sign. Flow switch. Forged steel. Forward scatter. Freight supply. Functional selector. Land station established for the safety of life (ITU designation).

FSA—Federal Security Agency.

FSC—Federal supply classification.

FSCC—Fire support coordination center.

FSCen—Flight service center.

FSCEPP—Functional section for consulting engineers in private practice (changed to PEPP).

FSCS—Flight service communications systems.

FSCT—Floyd Satellite Communications Terminal (Floyd, N.Y.).

FSE—Field support equipment.

FSF—Flight Safety Foundation.

FSGA—Four-wire, shipboard, general use, armored cable.

FSI—Frame sync indication.

FSK—Frequency-shift keying.

FSL—Federal stock listings.

FSM—Field-strength meter. Folded sideband modulation.

FSMWI—Free space microwave interferometer.

FSO—Full-scale output.

FSPE—Florida Society of Professional Engineers.

FSR—Feedback shift register.

FSRB—Flight Safety Review Board.

FSS—Federal supplies services. Flight service station (FAA).

FT—Fire Control Technician (U.S. Navy). Fluorescent target.

FTA—Film training aid.

FTC—Fast time constant. Flight test control station. Frequency time control.

ft-c—Foot-candle.

FTD—Foreign Technology Division (U.S. Air Force).

FTI—Frequency time indicator.

ft-l—Foot-lambert.

ft-lb—Foot-pound.

FTO—Flight test operations.

F to F—Face to face.

FTR—Film tracing reproduction.

FTS—Federal Telecommunications System. Float switch (NMTBA term). Foot switch (JIC term).

FTV—Flight test vehicle.

FTWG—Flight test working group.

FU—Fire unit. Fuse (JIC and NMTBA term).

FUIF—Fire unit integration facil-ity.

FUN—Function.

FUR—Failure, unsatisfactory or removal (report).

FVPB—Flight vehicle power branch (U.S. Air Force).

FW — Field weakening (JIC and NMTBA term). Full-wave.

FWA—Forward-wave amplifier.

FWAC—Full-wave alternating current.

FWDC—Full-wave direct current.

FWHM—Full width at half maximum.

FWR—Full-wave rectifier.

FWRU—Full-wave rectified unfiltered.

FWWMR—Fire-, water-, weather-, mildew-resistant.

FX—Extruded teflon. Fixed station (ITU designation).

FXBIN—Decimal to fixed binary translation.

FXE—Telemetering land station (ITU designation).

FY—Fiscal year.

G

G—Booster (Air Force vehicle designation). Digit. Fire control. Gate. Gauge. Gauss. Generator (JAN nomenclature). Generator/exciter/vibrator. Giga (prefix: 1,000,-000,000 or 10^9). Glass. Globular (pilot bulb designation). Government. Gravity. Grid. Ground vehicle (Air Force designation). Surface target (Dept. of Defense missile designation).

GA—Gas amplification. Glue acid. Go ahead. Good afternoon.

G/A—Ground-to-air.

G & C—Guidance and control.

G/A DL—Ground-to-air data link.

GAES—Gas Appliance Engineers' Society.

GAFB—Griffis Air Force Base.

G/A/G—Ground-air-ground.

GAI—Gate alarm indicator.

GAINS—Gimbal-less analytical inertial navigation system.

GAIT—Government and industry team.

GALV—Galvanized.

GAM—Guided aircraft missile.

GAMA—Gas Appliance Manufacturers' Association.

GAMAD—Gas monitor and adjuster.

GAMM—German-Swiss Applied Mathematics Society.

GAMMA—Generalized automatic

method of matrix assembly (computer matrix builder system developed by Bonner & Moore).

GAO—General Accounting Office.

GAP—General assembly program (computer program developed by General Electric).

GAPA—Ground-to-air pilotless aircraft.

GAPL—Group assembly parts list.

GAR—Guided aircraft rocket.

GARADE—Gathers, alarms, reports, displays, and evaluates (General Electric computer).

GASA—Georgia Aeronautics and Space Administration.

GASH—Guanidine aluminum sulfate hexahydrate (ferroelectrics).

GASP—Gevic arithmetic simulation program.

GAT—General aviation transponder. Greenwich apparent time. Ground-air transmitter.

GATR—Ground-air transmitter-receiver.

GATT—General agreement on tariffs and trade.

GAUSS—Gravity Association for Universal Scientific Study.

GAYIG—Gallium substituted yttrium iron garnet.

GB—Glide bomb. Ground backup relay.

GBL—Government bill of lading.

GBP—Gain-bandwidth product.

GBT—Graded-base transistors.

GBW—Gain-bandwidth product.

GC—Combined cotton and glass braid. Gas chromatography. Gigacycle per second (kilomegacycle per second). Great circle.

GCA—Ground control approach.

GCE—Ground control equipment.

GCI—Ground control interception.

GCMA—Government Contract Management Association of America, Inc. (425 Park Ave., New York, N.Y.).

GCO—Ground cutout.

GCR—Ground-controlled radar.

GCRE—Gas-cooled reactor experiment.

GCT—Great circle track. Greenwich civil time.

GD—Gate driver. Ground directional relay. Grown diffused.

GDA—Gun-defended area.

GDE—Ground data equipment.

GDF—Group distributing frames.

GDM—Geodetic distance measurement. Grid dip modulator.

GDNCE—Guidance.

GDO—Grid-dip oscillator.

GDOP—Geometric dilution of precision.

GDSA—Goldstone duplicate standard.

GE—Good evening.

GECENT—Postprocessor for the GE Mark Century control.

GECOM—General compiler (programming technique developed by General Electric).

GEE—Early British low-frequency version of loran. General evaluation equipment.

GEE H—Combination of the GEE and H systems of navigation.

GEEIA—Ground Electronics Engineering Installation Agency (Griffiss Air Force Base, New York).

GEEK—Geomagnetic electrokinetograph.

GEEP—General Electric electronic processor.

GEESE—General Electric's electronic system evaluator.

GEK—Geoelectrokinetograph.

GEM—Ground effect machines. Guidance evaluation missile.

GE/MAC—General Electric measurement and control.

GEON—Gyro-erected optical navigation (developed by Woods Hole Oceanographic Institution).

GEOREF—World geographic reference system.

GEP—Goddard experiment package.

GEPAC—General Electric programmable automatic comparator.

GERM—Ground-effect research machine (developed by Hawker-Siddeley).

GERSIS—General Electric range safety instrumentation system (U.S. Navy long-range tracking system).

GESAC—General Electric self-adaptive flight control.

GESOC—General Electric satellite orbit control.

GETIS—Ground Environment Team International Staff (NATO).

GETOL—Ground effect takeoff and landing (devleoped by General Dynamics).

GETR—General Electric test reactor.

GEV—Ground effect vehicle.

GeV—1,000,000,000 electron volts (1 GeV = 1 BeV).

GEVIC—General Electric variable increment computer.

GF—Generic failure rate. Glass braid and teflon-impregnated finish.

GFAE—Government-furnished aircraft equipment.

GFD—Gap-filler data.

GFE—Government-furnished equipment.

GFI—Gap-filler input.

GFMVT—General Foods moisture-vapor transmission test cabinet.

GFR—Gap-filler radar. Gas-filled rectifier.

GF/RP—Gap filler/reporting post.

GFT—Glass fabric tape.

GG — Double-glass braid. Groove gauge.

G/G—Ground-to-ground.

GGF—Double glass braid and teflon impregnation finish.

GGV—Double glass braid varnished.

GHA—Greenwich hour angle of Aries.

GHC—Generalized hyperbolic class.

GHE—Ground handling equipment.

GHOST—Global horizontal sounding technique.

GHSE—Ground handling and servicing equipment.

GI—Galvanized iron.

Gi—Gilbert.

GIAC—General Industry Advisory Committee.

GIFS—Gray Iron Founders' Society.

GIGI—Gamma inspection of grain integrity.

GIMRADA—Geodosy, Intelligence, and Mapping Research and Development Agency (U.S. Army, Corps of Engineers, Ft. Belvoir, Va.).

GIPER—Gamma - induced photon emitter.

GIPSE—Gravity-independent photosynthetic gas exchanger.

GIRD—Gruppa Isutcheniya Reaktivnovo Dvisheniya (Group for Investigation of Reaction Motion— Russain space-flight group formed in Nov., 1929).

GIRLS—Generalized information retrieval and listing system.

GIXU—Grain inspection X-ray unit.

GJ—Grown junction.

GK—Gyrocompass.

GL—Glass braid lacquered. Gun laying.

G/L—Gross weight-to-payload ratio.

GLEEP—Graphite low-energy experimental pile (Harwell, England).

GLIPAR—Guide line identification program for antimissile research (development of unorthodox missile defense — Technical Operations, Inc., Burlington, Mass.).

GLO—Ground liaison officer.

GLOBECOM—Global communications.

GLOMB—Glider bomb carrier.

GLOP—Gevic logic operation program.

GLOPAC—Gyroscopic low-power attitude control (developed by General Electric).

GLOTRAC—Global tracking.

GLS—General lighting service.

GLV—Gemini launch vehicle (NASA vehicle for Project Gemini).

GM—Gagemeter. Geometric mean. Good morning. Guided missile.

GMC—General Monte Carlo code.

GMD—Geometric mean distance.

GMDEP—Guided missile data exchange program.

GMK—Gyromagnetic compass.

GMR—Geometric mean radii.

GMS—Guided missile systems.

GMT—Greenwich mean time.

GN—Good night.

GND—Ground.

GNDCG — Commanding General —Army Ground Forces.

GNGCS—Chief of Staff — Army Ground Forces.

GNI—Gross national income.

GNL—Georgia Nuclear Laboratories.

GNP—Gross national product.

GNTR—Generator.

GO—Goniometer (JAN nomenclature).

GOAT—Gerber oscillogram amplitude translator.

GOC—Ground Observer Corps.

GOCR—Gated-off controlled rectifier.

GOE—Ground operating equipment.

GOR—General operational requireputer term).

GOR—General operational requirement.

GOSS—Ground operational support system.

GOX—Gaseous oxygen.

GP—General purpose. Ground rods (JAN nomenclature).

GPA—General-purpose amplifier.

GPATS—General-purpose automatic test system.

GPC—General-purpose computer. Geocentric pendulum control (developed by Lear, Inc., Grand Rapids, Mich.).

GPDC — General - purpose digital computer.

GPG—General planning group.

GPH—Gallons per hour.

GPI—Ground position indicator.

GPN—General performance number.

GPO—General Post Office (British). Government Printing Office.

GPS—General problem solver. General-purpose simulation.

GPSSM—General-purpose surface-to-surface missile.

GPU—Generating power unit. Ground power unit.

GR—Gas ratio. Grown rate.

GRACE—Group routing and charging equipment (British telephone term).

GRAD—Gradient.

GRAVIENTOMETER — Gravitation gradient meter.

GRD—Geophysics Research Directorate (Air Force Cambridge Research Laboratory). Ground (JIC and NMTBA term).

GREB—Galactic radiation experiment background (U.S. satellite program).

GRP—Group.

GRS—General radio service (Canadian counterpart of U.S. Citizens-band radio).

GR - VC - IC—Graphic Reproductions-Visual Communications Industries' Council.

GS—Genearl staff. Geological survey. Ground speed. Group selector (telephone term).

GSA—General Services Administration.

GSC—General Staff Corps.

GSDF—Ground Self-Defense Force (Japan).

GSDS—Goldstone duplicate standard.

GSE—Ground support equipment.

GSETD—General systems engineering and technical direction.

GSFC—Goddard Space Flight Center (division of NASA, Greenbelt, Md.).

GSI—Government source inspection. Ground speed indicator.

GSK—Concrete barge used as floating warehouse (U.S. Navy).

GSO—Ground safety officer.

GSR—Galvanic skin resistance.

GSS—Global surveillance system.

GSSO—General Stores Supply Office (Navy Bureau, Philadelphia, Pa.).

GST—Greenwich sidereal time.

GT—Gas turbine. Glow tube. Gross ton.

GTC—Gain time control.

GTCP—Gas turbine compressor.

GTER—Gate turnoff controlled rectifier.

GTG—Gas turbine generator.

GTO—Gas tube, sign and oil burner ignition cable. Gate turn-off switch.

GTRP—General transpose (Philco 2000 computer term).

GTS—Gas-turbine ship.

GTT—Generated target tracking.

GTTS—Gyro transfer table system (developed by Sperry).

GTV—Guided test vehicle.

GTW—Gross takeoff weight.

GUBI—Gemeinschaft Unabhangiger Beratender Ingenieurbueros (association of German consulting firms).

GUSTO—Guidance using stable tuning oscillations.

GW—Galvanized steel wire shield.

GWETA—Greater Washington (D.C.) Educational TV Association.

GWT—Gross weight.

GZ—Ground zero.

H

H—Amateur. Halt. Hand-actuated. Hardware. Head, hand and chest sets (JAN nomenclature). Heater. Hecto—(prefix: 100 or 10^2). High power. Hostile. Nondirectional radio homing beacon (50-2000 watts). Silo (Air Force designation).

h—Henry (unit of inductance). Hour.

HA—Half add. Half adder. Heavy artillery.

HAAW—Heavy attack / assault weapon (U.S. Army).

HAD—Horizontal array of dipoles.

HADC—Holloman Air Development Center.

HA-Dec—Hour angle - declination (Harvard University radiotelescope).

HAE—High-altitude emergency.

HAF—High abrasion furnace.

HAFB—Holloman Air Force Base.

HAM—High-speed automatic monitor (manufactured by Monitor Systems, Inc., Ft. Washington, Pa.).

HAPO—Hanford atomic products

operations (Atomic Energy Commission installation).

HARC—Hudson Amateur Radio Council.

HARCO—Hyperbolic area control.

HARD—High-altitude relay point.

HARP—High-altitude research program (McGill University, Montreal, Canada).

HAS—High-altitude sampler.

HASL—Health and Safety Laboratory (U.S. Atomic Energy Commission).

HASP—High-altitude sampling program.

HAV—Hot air vulcanization (used in curing wire insulation).

HAWK—Homing all the way killer (solid-propellant radar homing missile, developed by Raytheon for U.S. Army).

HB—Heavy bombardment. High boilers. Homing beacon.

HBC—Honeywell business compiler.

HC—Crystal holder (JAN nomenclature). Heater cord. Hospital Corps. Hour circle.

HCHC—High carbon, high chrome.

HCP—Hexagonal close-packed. Horizontal candle power.

HCPS—Horizontal candle-power seconds.

HCT—Heater center tap.

HD—Air-conditioning apparatus (JAN nomenclature). Heavy duty. Horizontal drive.

HDA—Heavy-duty amplifier.

HDD—Human disorientation device (a machine at the U.S. Navy School of Aviation Medicine, Pensacola, Fla.).

HDDS—High-density data system.

HDEP—High-density electronic packaging.

HDF—High-frequency direction finding.

HDT—Heat distortion temperature.

HE—High explosive.

HEAP—Helicopter extended area platform.

HEC—Hollerith electronic computer (built by The British Tabulating Machine Co.).

HEF—High-energy forming.

HEI—Human Engineering Institute.

HEL—Helitron.

HEM—Hybrid electromagnetic.

HEPC—Hydroelectric Power Commission.

HEP DEX—High-energy proton-detection experiment.

HERALD—Harbor echo-ranging and listening device.

HERF—High energy rate forming.

HERO—Hazards of electromagnetic radiation to ordnance (project conducted by Naval Weapons Lab at Dahlgren, Va.).

HES—Home Entertainment Service (pay TV system).

HETS—Hyper-environmental test system.

HEW—Dept. of Health, Education and Welfare (U.S. Government).

HEX—Hexagonal.

HF—Heavy formvar magnet wire. Height-finding. High frequency. Hold fire.

HFBR—High flux beam reactor.

HFC—High-frequency correction.

HF-DF—High-frequency direction finder.

HFI—High Fidelity Institute, Inc.

HFIR—High flux isotope reactor.

HFR—High flux reactor.

HG—Harmonic generator.

HGR—High group receiving unit.

HGT—High Group transmitting unit.

HH—Nondirectional radio homing beacon (2000 watts or over).

H-HOUR—Hour for attack, assault wave or movement to begin.

HI—High. Telegraphic laugh (CW abbreviation).

HI-AR—High aromatic.

HIBAL—High altitude balloon.

HICAPCOM—High-capacity communications (U.S. Navy system).

HIDAN—High-density air navigation (developed by Genearl Precision Laboratories).

HIFAR—High-flux heavy water reactor.

HIFI—High intensity food irradiator (Quartermaster Corps, Sharpe General Depot, Lathrop, Calif.).

HIG—Hermetic integrating gyro.

HILAC—Heavy-ion linear accelerator.

HIPAC—Hitachi parametron automatic computer (manufactured by Hitachi, Ltd., Japan).

HIPAR—High - power acquisition radar (produced by General Electric Co.'s HMED).

HIPERNAS — High - performance navigation system. Inertial guidance system developed by Bell Aerosystems Co.).

HIPO—Hospital indicator for physicians' orders.

HIPS—Hyper - intense proximal scanning (ultrasonic cleaning device).

HIPSA—Hallicrafters incremental power spectrum analyzer.

HIRAN—High-precision short-range navigation system.

HIRDL—High Intensity Radiation Development Lab (Brookhaven, N.Y.).

HITAC—Hitachi computer (developed by Hitachi, Ltd., Japan).

HITMP—Highest temperature.

HIVOS—High vacuum orbital simulator (developed by Lockheed).

HJ—Station open from sunrise to sunset; day station (ITU designation). Utility helicopter (U.S. Navy).

HL—Heater tap for panel lamp. High-level.

HLB—Hydrophile-lipophile balance (an emulsifier's attraction for either oil or water).

HLD—Hold.

HLT—Halt.

HM—Heater mid - tap. Hospital corpsman (U.S. Navy).

HMI—Handbook of maintenance instructions.

HMSO—Honolulu Magnetic and Seismological Observatory (center for compass calibration and seismic sea warning for the Pacific).

HMTS—Her Majesty's Telegraph Ship (for laying underwater cable).

HMW—Height-of-maxwind.

HN—Training helicopter (U.S. Navy).

HNC—Higher National Certificate (British school certificate).

HND—Higher National Diploma (British school diploma). Hundred.

HO—Hydrographic Office (U.S. Navy). Observation helicopter (U.S. Navy).

HON—Hold-off normal contact springs.

HOPE—Hydrogen-oxygen primary extraterrestrial fuel cell program (developed by General Electric for U.S. Air Force).

HOT—Horizontal output transformer. Horizontal output tube.

HP—Haut - parleur (loudspeaker-French). Heptode. High-pass. High-performance. High pressure.

HPD—Hard point defense. Heater cord.

HPF—Highest possible frequency.

hp-hr—Horsepower-hour.

HPMV—High-pressure mercury vapor.

HPN—All-neoprene heater cord. Hydraulic-pneumatic trailer.

HR—Heater. Height range. Here.

Hour. Transport helicopter (U.S. Navy).

HRAF—Human relations area files (informational retrieval system—Yale University).

HRE—Homogeneous reactor experiment (Oak Ridge, Tenn.).

HRH—High rate heat.

HRI—Height-range indicator.

HRIR—High - resolution infrared radiometer.

HRT—Homogeneous reactor test.

HRZN—Horizon.

HS—Half subtractor. Handset. Heater shield. Hydrofoil ship. Jacketed heater cord.

HSCA—Horizontal sweep circuit analyzer.

HSFS—High-Speed Flight Station Edwards, Calif.).

HSI—High-strand-intensity (high-strength glass reinforcement developed by Owens-Corning). Horizontal situation indicator.

HSJ—Rubber-jacketed heater cord.

HSM—Hardened silo strategic missile.

HSP—High-speed printer.

HSRO—High-speed repetitive operation.

HSRS—Hurricane supersonic research site.

HSS—High speed steel.

HST—Harmonic and spurious totalizer.

HT—Hautes tensions (B+–French). Headed type. Headset. Headset/telephone receiver. Heat treatment. Heater tap. Height technician. Height telling. High temperature. High tension (B+–British).

HTA—Heavier-than-air.

HTB—Holt buffer transfer.

HTC—Hydrofoil test craft.

HTFMI—Heat Transfer and Fluid Mechanics Institute.

HTGR—High-temperature gas-cooled reactor.

H-T-H-W—High-temperature, hot-water.

HTL—High - temperature lacquer. Hotel call, time and charges mandatory (telephone term).

HTM—Hard-tube modulator.

HTN—Heterodyne.

HTO—Horizontal takeoff.

HTOHL—Horizontal takeoff, horizontal landing.

HTP—High-test hydrogen peroxide. Trunnion hydrogen peroxide.

HTRE—Heat transfer reactor experiment.

HTV—Hypersonic test vehicle.

HUFF-DUFF—High - frequency direction finder.

HUK — Hunter - killer (Antisubmarine naval force).

HUKP—Hostile, unknown, faker and pending (SAGE term).

HV—High voltage.

HVAR — High - velocity aircraft rocket.

HVDC—High-voltage direct current.

HVDF—High and very high frequency direction finding.

HVL—Half-value layer.

HVPS—High-voltage power supply.

HVR—High-vacuum rectifier.

HW—Half-wave. Heavy wall.

HX—Hexode. High index. Station with no specific working hours (ITU designation).

HY—Hybrid coil/hybrid junction.

hy—Henry.

HYCOL—Hybrid computer link (developed by General Electric).

HY-COM—Highway communications system (developed by Delco).

HYCOTRAN—Hybrid computer translator.

HYD—Hydraulic.

HYDAC—Hybrid digital - analog computer (developed by Electronic Associates, Inc.).

HYDAPT—Hybrid digital- **[Cont.]**

analog pulse time (developed by General Electric Co.).

HYDRO—Hydrographic. Hydrographic office.

HYG—Hygroscopic.

HYPERAN—Electronic bombing system.

HYPO—High-power water-boiler reactor (Los Alamos, N. Mex.).

HYPREM—Hyper-response electric motor.

HYSCAN—Hybrid scanning radar system.

Hz—Hertz.

I

I—Current. Iconoscope. Indicating. Indicator. Industrial. Intercept-defense (Air Force mission designation). Miscellaneous indicating parts.

IA—Initial appearance.

IAA—International Academy of Astronautics (established in 1960 by the International Astronomical Federation).

IAAC—International Association for Analog Computation (Association Internationale Pour Le Calcul Analogique (50 Avenue Franklin Roosevelt, Bruxelles 5, Belgium).

IAARC—International Administrative Aeronautical Radio Conference.

IACC—Industrial Analysis and Control Council.

IACE—Illinois Association of Consulting Engineers.

IACOMS—International Advisory Committee on Marine Sciences (UNESCO).

IACS—International Arms-Control Symposium. International annealed copper standard.

IAD—Initiation area discriminator. International Astrophysical Decade.

IAE—Integral of absolute error. Integrated absolute error.

IAEA—International Atomic Energy Agency.

IAEI—International Association of Electrical Inspectors (612 N. Michigan Ave., Chicago, Ill.).

IAEL—International Association of Electrical Leagues.

IAESTE—International Association for the Exchange of Students for Technical Experience (29 W. 39th St., New York 18, N.Y.).

IAF—International Astronautical Federation.

IAGC—Instantaneous automatic gain control.

IAGS — Inter - American Geodetic Survey.

IAL—International Algebraic Language (former name of ALGOL).

IAM—Institute of Appliance Manufacturers.

IAMS—Instantaneous audience measurement system.

IAO—Internal automation operation.

IAP—Initial approach.

IAPG—Interagency Advanced Power Group (formerly Interservice Group for Flight Vehicle Power — includes NASA, AES, and ARPA).

IAPO—International Association of Physical Oceanography.

IAS—Indian Astronautical Society. Indicated air speed. Institute of the Aeronautical Sciences.

IASA—Insurance Accounting and Statistical Association.

IAT—Individual acceptance test.

IATA—International Air Transport Association.

IATCS—International Air Traffic Communication Station.

IATSE—International Alliance of Theatrical Stage Employees (1270 6th Ave., New York, N.Y.).

IAU—International Astronomical Union.

IAVC—Instantaneous automatic volume control.

IAW—In accordance with.

IB—International broadcasting.

IBBM—Iron body bronze (or brass) mounted.

IBEW—International Brotherhood of Electrical Workers (union).

IBO — International Broadcasting Organization.

IBR—Integral boiling reactor.

IBRD—International Bank for Reconstruction and Development.

IBRL—Initial bomb release line.

IBT—Instrumented bend test.

IC—Initial condition. Inlet contact. Input circuit. Instruction counter. Interchange center. Intercommunication drum (SAGE term). Internal connection. International control.

I & C—Installation and checkout.

ICA—Industrial Communications Association. International Cooperation Administration.

ICAO—International Civil Aviation Organization.

ICAS—Intermittent commercial and amateur service. International Council of the Aeronautical Sciences.

ICBM—Intercontinental ballistic missile.

ICC — International Computation Center (to be set up in Rome, Italy).

ICCPC—International Computation Center's Preparatory Committee.

ICDO—International Civil Defense Organization.

ICE—Input-checking equipment. Institution of Civil Engineers (British organization).

ICECAN — Iceland - Canada telephone cable.

ICER—Infrared cell, electronically refrigerated (developed by Borg-Warner Research Center).

ICES—International Council for the Exploration of the Sea.

ICESC—Industry Crew Escape Systems Committee.

ICET—Institute for the Certification of Engineering Technicians (National Society of Professional Engineers).

ICF—Intercommunication flip-flop.

IChemE—Institution of Chemical Engineers (British organization).

ICI—Investment Casting Institute.

ICIP—International Conference on Information Processing.

ICITA—International Cooperative Investigations of the Tropical Atlantic.

ICL—Incoming line.

ICME—International Conference on Medical Electronics.

ICMST—International Conference on Machine Searching and Translation (sponsored by Westren Reserve University and Rand Corp.).

ICNF—Irredundant conjunctive normal formula.

ICO—Interagency Committee on Oceanography.

ICOLD—International Commission on Large Dams.

ICPAC—Instantaneous compressor performance analysis computer.

ICR—Instantaneous center of rotation. International Congress of Radiology.

ICRP—International Commission on Radiological Protection.

ICRU—International Commission on Radiological Units and **[Cont.]**

Measurements.

ICSU—International Council of Scientific Unions (UNESCO).

ICT—Insulating core transformer.

ICTASD—International Convention on Transistors and Associated Semiconductor Devices.

ICTD—Interchannel time displacement.

ICW—Interrupted continuous wave.

ID—Identification. Indicating device (JAN nomenclature). Information distributor. Intermodulation distortion. Item description.

IDA—Immediate damage assessment. Institute for Defense Analysis. Integrodifferential analyzer. International Development Association. Iterative differential analyzer.

IDACON—Iterative differential analyzer cotnrol.

IDAP—Iterative differential analyzer pinboard.

IDAS—Iterative differential analyzer slave.

IDEP—Interservice data exchange program (developed by Librascope Div., General Precision, Inc.).

IDF—Integrated data file. Intermediate distributing frame.

IDFR—Identification friendly.

IDHS—Intelligence data handling system.

IDI—Improved data interchange. Industrial Designers' Institute.

IDIOT—Instrumentation digital on-line transcriber (developed by Rocketdyne).

IDNF—Irredundant disjunctive normal formula.

IDO—Identification officer.

IDP—Industrial data processing. Integrated data processing. Intermodulation distortion percentage.

IDS—Identification section. Identification supervisor.

IE—Internal environment (reliability term).

IEA—Instruments, Electronics, and Automation Exhibition (held every two years in London).

IEC—International Electrotechnical Commission.

IECEJ—Institute of Electrical Communications Engineers of Japan.

IEE—Institution of Electrical Engineers (British organization). Institute of Environmental Engineers.

IEM—Ion-exchange membrane.

IEP—Instrument for evaluation of photographs.

IES—Illuminating Engineering Society (1860 Broadway, New York 23, N.Y.). Institute of Environmental Sciences.

IESA—Indiana Electronic Service Association.

IET—Initial engine test.

IETF—Initial engine test facility.

IF—Information collector.

IFAC—International Federation on Automatic Control.

IFALPA—International Federation of Airline Pilots' Associations.

IFATCA—International Federation of Air Traffic Controllers' Associations.

IFC—Instantaneous frequency correlation. Integrated fire control. International Finance Corp.

IFEMS—International Congress of the Federation of Electron Microscope Societies.

IFF—Identification, friend or foe.

IFI—Industrial Fasteners Institute (1517 Terminal Tower, Cleveland, Ohio).

IFIPS—International Federation of Information Processing Societies.

IFLC—International Frequency List Committee (ITU).

IFME—International Federation for Medical Electronics.

IFN—Information.

IFORS—International Federation of Operational Research Societies (11 Park Lane, London W.1., England).

IFP—International fixed public.

IFPM—In-flight performance monitoring.

IFR—In-flight refueling. Instrument flight rules.

IFRB—International Frequency Registration Board (ITU).

IFRO—Internal feedrate override (numerical control term).

IFS—Inshore fire support. Integrated flight system. Interrelated flow simulation.

IFSS — International flight service station.

IGC—International geophysical cooperation. Isothermal gas chromatography.

IGESUCO—Infrastruction Ground Environment Subcommitee (NATO).

IGI—Inner grid injection.

IGOR—Instrument ground - based optical recording. Intercept ground optical recorder (developed by the American Optical Co.).

IGY—International Geophysical Year.

IGY WDC—International Geophysical Year, World Data Center.

IHEA—Industrial Heating Equipment Association.

IHF—Inhibit halt flip-flop (computer term).

IHFM—Institute of High Fidelity Manufacturers.

IHP—Indicated horsepower.

IIOE—International Indian Ocean Expedition.

IIR—Integrated instrumentation radar. Intermediate infrared.

IISL—International Institute of Space Law.

IL—Indicating light (NMTBA

term). Insulators (JAN nomenclature).

ILAS—Instrument low-approach system.

ILCCS—Integrated launch control and checkout system.

ILG—Instrument-landing guidance.

ILLIAC—Illinois automatic computer (University of Illinois).

ILMAC—International Exhibition and Congress of Laboratory, Measurements, and Automation Techniques in Chemistry.

ILPF—Ideal low-pass filter.

ILS—Instrument landing system.

ILSAP—Instrument landing system approach.

IM—Instrumentation (U.S. Navy). Intensity-measuring device (JAN nomenclature). Interceptor missile. VHF boundary marker (FAA).

IMC—Image motion compensation. Instrument meterological conditions.

IMCC—Integrated Mission Control Center (NASA-manned spacecraft center, Houston, Texas).

IMCO—International Metered Communications.

IMechE—Institution of Mechanical Engineers (British organization).

IMF—Internal magnetic focus. International monetary fund.

IMFSS—Integrated missile flight safety system.

IMHEP—Ideal man-helicopter engineering project (Bell Helicopter Co., Fort Worth, Texas).

IMKR—Inner marker (instrument landing system).

IMO—Improper order alarm.

IMP — Inflatable micrometeoroid paraglider (produced by Space-General for NASA). Instrumented monkey pod (project on space environment conducted by North American Aviation, Inc.). **[Cont.]**

Interplanetary monitoring probe.

IMPACT—Implementation, planning, and control technique.

IMS—Image-motion simulator (manufactured by Fairchild Camera and Instrument Corp.). Industrial Management Society. Institute of Management Sciences.

IMSA—International Municipal Signal Association (130 W. 42nd St., New York 36, N.Y.).

IMST—Institute of Marine Sciences and Technology.

IMU—Inertial measurement unit.

IN—Input.

INACS—Interstate Airways Communications Station.

INCA—Integrated navigation and communication, automatic.

INCH—Integrated chopper.

INCR—Increase. Increment.

IND—Indicator. Inductance. Intercept director (SAGE term).

INF—Irredundant normal formula.

ING—Inertial Navigation Gyro.

INIC—Current negative-impedance converter.

INS—Inertial navigation system. Interstation noise suppression.

INSA—Institute National de Science Applique' (French agency).

INSACS—Interstate airway communications station.

INSMETLS—International shielding metals (for gamma radiation).

INSSCC—Interim National Space Surveillance Control Center.

INST—Instrument.

INSTAR—Inertialess scanning, tracking and ranging (radar system developed for U.S. Army Signal Corps by W. L. Maxson Co.).

INSTLN—Installation.

INT—Interphone. Interrogate. Interrupt. Interrupter. Intersection.

INT CON—Internal connection.

INTCP—Intercept.

INTEL—Intelligence.

INTERDICT—Interference detection and interdiction by countermeasures team.

INTERMAG—International Conference on Nonlinear Magnetics.

INTFC—Interference.

INTL—International.

INTRAFAX—Facsimile system for private use (Western Union).

INV—Inverter.

IO—Image orthicon. Injector orifice (rocket term). Iterative operation.

I/O—Input/output.

IOB—Input-output buffer.

IOC—Initial operational capability. In-out converter (computer term). Intergovernmental Oceanographic Commission (UNESCO).

IOCS—Input-output control system.

IOL—Instantaneous overload (JIC term).

ION—Institute of Navigation.

IOP—Input/output processor.

IOPS—Input-output programming system.

IOR—Input-output register.

IORU—International Commission on Radiological Units and Measurements.

IOS—Indian Ocean ship (Project Mercury tracking ship). Input-output skip. International Organization for Standardization.

IOTA—Information overload testing apparatus.

IOU—Immediate operational use.

IOVST—International Organization for Vacuum Science and Technology (U.S. address: 1515 Sedgwick Street, Chicago 10, Ill.).

IP—Cathode-ray-tube indicator. (JAN nomenclature). Identification of position. Identification point. Index of performance. Industrial production. Initial point. Item processing.

IPA—Intermediate power amplifier.

IPB—Illustrated parts breakdown.

Inert processing building (Naval missile assembly building).

IPBM—Interplanetary ballistic missile.

IPC—Institute of Paper Chemistry (Appleton, Wis.). Institute of Printed Circuits.

IPCEA—Insulated Power Cable Engineers' Association.

IPD—Insertion phase delay.

IPDP—Intervals of pulsations of diminishing period (geomagnetic term).

IPE—Interpret parity error.

IPET—Independent Professional Electronic Technicians (California TV service organization).

IPI—Identified friendly prior to interception.

IPL—Identified parts list. Information-processing language.

IPM—Impulses per minute. Incidental phase modulation.

IPN—Inspection progress notifications.

IPPMA—In-plant Powder Metallurgy Association.

IPRO—International Patent Research Office.

IProdE—Institution of Production Engineers (British organization).

IPS—Impact predictor system. Inches per second (tape speed). Instrumentation power system. Iron pipe size.

IPY—International Polar Year.

IQSY—International Quiet Sun Year.

IR—Information retrieval. Instruction register.

I-R—Interrogator-responder.

IRAC—Interdepartment Radio Advisory Committee (Office of Defense Mobilization, Washington 25, D.C.).

IRAR—Impulse response area ratio.

IRASER—Infrared amplification by stimulated emission of radiation.

IRBM—Intermediate-range ballistic missile.

IRC—Infrared countermeasures. International reply coupon.

IRCC—International Radio Consultative Committee (ITU).

IRCCM—Infrared counter-countermeasures.

IRE—Institute of Radio Engineers (1 E. 79th St., New York 21, N.Y.).

IREP — Interdisciplinary research equipment program.

IRFB—International Radio Frequency Board (ITU).

IRFNA—Inhibited red fuming nitric acid (missile fuel oxidizer).

IRGAR—Infrared gas radiation.

IRI—Integrated range instrumentation system.

IRIA—Infrared Information and Analysis Center (Willow Run Labs of the University of Michigan).

IRIG—Interrange Instrumentation Group (Dept. of Defense).

IRIS—Infrared Information Symposia.

IRMA—Infrared miss-distance approximator.

IRMP—Interservice Radiation Measurement Program (sponsored by Advanced Research Projects Agency).

IRP—Initial receiving point.

IRPM—Infrared physical measurement.

IRRAD—Infrared range and detection.

IRS—Ineligible reserve section.

IRSP—Infrared spectrometer.

IRTF—Intermediate Range Task Force (committee on data systems languages).

IRTRAN—Infrared transmitting.

IRTWG—Inter-range telem-[Cont.]

etry working group.

IRU—Inertial reference unit.

IRW—International Rocket Week.

IS—Infrasonic. Initiation supervisor. Insulating sleeve. Internal shield. Interval signal.

I/S—Interference per kilocycle to the signal carrier power of a receiver.

ISA—Ignition and separation assembly (rocket term). Instrument Society of America.

ISAF—Intermediate super-abrasion furnace.

ISB—Independent sideband.

ISC—International Space Congress.

ISCAN—Inertialess steerable communications antenna (developed by U.S. Signal Corps and AVCO).

ISCT—Ito system color TV (Japanese development).

ISD—International subscriber dialing.

ISE—Integral squared error. Interpret sign error.

ISEEP—Infrared Sensitive Element Evaluation Program (U.S. Naval Ordnance Laboratory, Corona, Calif.).

ISG—Interconnected Systems Group. Interservice Group.

ISIC—Inter-symbol interference corrector.

ISIS—Integrated strike and interceptor system.

ISL—Institute of Space Law (established in 1960 by the International Astronautical Federation).

ISM—Industrial, scientific, and medical (FCC term). Initial segment membrane.

ISO—Individual system operation. International Organization for Standardization. International Science Organization.

ISP—Italian Society of Physics.

ISR—Information storage and re-

trieval. Institute of Semiconductor Research (Leningrad, USSR). Integral nuclear superheat reactor.

ISRAC—ITT secure ranging and communication system.

ISRSM—International Symposium on Rocket and Satellite Meteorology.

ISS—Institute For Strategic Studies (Ford Foundation group in England).

ISSE—International Sight and Sound Exposition.

ISTAR—Image storage translation and reproduction (developed by Chance Vought Corp.).

ISU—International Scientific Union.

IT—Input translator. Intensity of telephone interference. Item transfer.

ITAE—Integrated product of time and absolute error.

ITDE—Interchannel (intertrack) time displacement error.

ITE—Institute of Telecommunications Engineers.

ITG—Institute Technical Groups (AIEE specialist groups).

ITL—Integrated transfer and launch. Integration, test, and launch.

ITOR—Intercept target optical reader.

ITP—Integrated test program.

ITPA—Independent Telephone Pioneer Association (Room 406, Ferguson Bldg., Springfield, Ill.).

ITS—Integrated trajectory system.

ITSO—Instrument Technician Service Organization (Baltimore, Md.).

ITTA—Indianapolis Television Technician's Association.

ITU—International Telecommunications Union.

ITV—Industral televison.

ITVAC—Industrial transistor value automatic computer (developed by

Industro Transistor Corp.).

ITVB—International television broadcasting.

ITVSDA—Independent TV Service Dealers' Association (213 S. Coronado St., Los Angeles, Calif.).

IUB—International Union of Biochemistry.

IUE—International Union of Electrical, Radio and Machine Workers (AFL-CIO).

IUGG—International Union of Geodesy and Geophysics. (UNESCO).

IUPAC—International Union of Pure and Applied Chemistry.

IUPAP—International Union of Pure and Applied Physics.

IUTAM—International Union of Theoretical and Applied Mechanics.

IV—Inverter.

IVVI—Instantaneous vertical velocity indicator.

IWE—Institution of Water Engineers (British).

IWRC—Independent wire rope core.

IWST—Integrated weapons system training.

IX—Unclassified vessel (U.S. Navy).

J

J—Integer. Jack/connector/plug/receptacle. Jog (NMTBA term). Joule. Junction device (JAN nomenclature). Spacecraft (Air Force vehicle designation). Square root of −1.

JA—Jump address.

JAAF—Joint Army-Air Force.

JACC—Joint automatic control conference.

JADE—Japan area defense environment (radar system developed by Litton Industries, Van Nuys, Calif.).

JAERI—Japan Atomic Energy Research Institute.

JAG—Judge Advocate General.

JAMMAT—Joint American Military Mission for Aid to Turkey.

JAN—Joint Army-Navy.

JANAF—Joint Army-Navy-Air Force.

JANAP—Joint Army-Navy-Air Force Publication.

JARS—Joliet Amateur Radio Society (Joliet, Ill.).

JASDA—Julie automatic sonic data analyzer (automatic sonar ana-

lyzing equipment developed by Douglas Aircraft).

JASTOP—Jet assist stop.

JATO—Jet-assisted takeoff.

JBES—Jodrell Bank Experimental Station (Cheshire, England).

JCAE—Joint Committee on Atomic Energy (U. S. Congress).

JCC—Joint communications center.

JCET—Joint Council on Educational Television.

JCS—Joint Chiefs of Staff.

JCTN—Junction.

JDA—Japanese Defense Agency.

JDC—Job description card.

JEC—Japanese Electrotechnical Committee (Japanese member of International Electrotechnical Committee).

JECMB—Joint Executive Committee on Medicine and Biology.

JEDEC—Joint Electron Device Engineering Council.

JEDS—Japanese expeditions to the deep sea.

JEIA—Japanese Electronic Industries Association.

JEIDA—Japan Electronic   **[Cont.]**

Industry Development Association.

JEPIA—Japan Electronic Parts Industry Association.

JESSI—Junior Engineers' and Scientists' Summer Institute.

JETEC—Joint Electron Tube Engineering Council.

JETRO—Japan External Trade Research Organization (original name, 1951; later reorganized as Japan External Trade Recovery Organization; now Japan Export Trade Promotion Agency.

JETS—Junior Engineering Technical Society.

JFAC—Joint flight acceptance component testing.

JGN—Junction gate number.

JIC—Joint Industrial Conference.

JICHS—Joint Industrial Conference on Hydraulic Standards.

JIEE—Japanese Institute of Electrical Engineers.

JILA—Joint Institute for Laboratory Astrophysics (National Bureau of Standards, Boulder, Colo.).

JIS—Japanese Industrial Standard.

JLPC—Joint Logistics Planning Committee.

JLRSE—Joint long-range strategic estimate.

JMI—Japan Machinery and Metals Inspection Institute.

JMSAC—Joint Meteorological Satellite Advisory Committee.

JNCG—Japan Nuclear Codes Group.

JNWPU—Joint Numerical Weather Prediction Unit (Weather Bureau, Suitland, Md.).

JOC—Joint Operations Center.

JOR—Jet operations requirements.

JOVIAL—Jules' own version of the international algebraic language.

JPL—Jet Propulsion Laboratory.

JPM—Jet piercing machine (rocket used in mining).

JPTO—Jet-propelled takeoff.

JS—Justified.

JSCP—Joint strategic capabilities plan.

JSDA—Japanese Self-Defense Agency.

JSOP—Joint strategic objective plan.

JSRCSC—Joint Services Radio Component Standardization Committee (British).

JSSC—Joint Services Standardization Committee (British).

JTAC—Joint Technical Advisory Committee.

JTF—Joint Task Force.

JUG—Joint Users' Group. (Computer users' association affiliated with the Association for Computing Machinery).

K

K—Braided heavy-duty cord. Cathode. Faker (known friendly aircraft simulating an enemy during an air defense training mission). Karma. Kilo-(prefix: 1,000 or 10^3). Klystron. Relay. Solar absorption index. Tanker (Air Force mission designation). Wahl factor.

Ka—Auroral absorption index.

KAFB—Keesler Air Force Base.

KAPL—Knoll's Atomic Power Laboratory (operated for the AEC by General Electric).

KB—Keyboard.

KCC—Keyboard common contact.

Kd—Absorption index for a route longer than 4,000 kilometers.

KDP—Potassium dihydrogen phosphate (a ferroelectric material).

KES—Kansas Engineering Society.

KeV—Kiloelectron volts (1,000 electron volts).

KEWB—Kinetic experiment on water boilers (nuclear test providing 530,000 kw—performed by AEC).

KhPI—Khimicheskii poglotitel izvestkovyi (chemical absorbent, calcareous—Russian term).

KIFIS—Kollsman integrated flight instrument system.

KIMCODE—Kimble method for controlled devacuation (TV picture tubes).

KISS—Keep it simple, sir.

KLA—Klyston amplifier.

KLO—Klystron oscillator.

Km—Absoprtion index for an entirely daylight path at the path midpoint.

Kmc—Kilomegacycles per second.

KMER—Kodak metal etch resist (manufactured by Eastman Kodak Co., Rochester, N. Y.).

KMS—Keysort multiple selectors (telephone term).

KOR—Kodak ortho resist.

KP—Key pulsing.

KPR—Kodak photo resist (for etched circuits; manufactured by Eastman Kodak Co.).

KRS—Kristalle aus dem Schmelzfluss (crystals from the melting pot: infrared crystals—German.

KT—Kiloton. Knot (nautical mile per hour).

KTR—Keyboard typing reperforator.

KvP—Kilovolt peak (unit of output capacity of X-ray equipment).

KWESTEVDET—Key West Test and Evaluation Detachment.

KWIC—Keyword in context.

KY—Keying device (JAN nomenclature).

L

L—Inductance. Inductor/choke/coil. Lamberts. Large. Left. Level. Lift. Listening. Load. Looper. Loran. Lost (air defense radar expression). Low. Low power. Tie-line unit (telephone term).

LA—Latin America. Left ascension. Link allotter.

LAB—Low-altitude bombing.

LABIL—Light aircraft binary information link (developed by Stromberg-Carlson).

LABPIE—Low-altitude bombing position indicator equipment (developed by NADC, Johnsville, Pa.).

LABROC—Laboratory rocket propellant evaluator (developed by Astrosystems, Inc.).

LABS—Low-altitude bombing system.

LAC—Load accumulator.

LACE—Liquid air collection engine. Liquid air cycle engine (developed by Marquardt Corp.).

LACES—Los Angeles Council of Engineering Societies.

LACR—Low-altitude coverage radar.

LACT—Lease automatic custody transfer.

LADAR—Laser doppler radar.

LADD—Low-angle drogued delivery.

LADIZ—Leaving air defense identification zone.

LAEC—Los Angeles Electric Club.

LAFTA—Latin American Free Trade Area.

LAL—Lower acceptance level.

LAM—Load accumulator with magnitude.

LAMA—Local automatic message accounting (telephone term).

LAMP—Library addition and maintenance (developed by Minneapolis-Honeywell). Lunar analysis and mapping program (U. S. Army Corps of Engineer project).

LAMPRE—Los Alamos molten plutonium reactor experiment.

LANAC—Laminar navigation and anticollision.

LANNET—Large artificial nerve network.

LANTCOM—Atlantic Command.

LAR—Liquid air rocket.

LARC—Lighter, amphibious, resupply, cargo (15-ton U. S. Army wheeled amphibian built by Ingersoll Kalamazoo Div. of Borg-Warner Corp. for U. S. Army Transportation Corps). Livermore advanced research computer (constructed by Sperry Rand).

LARCT—Last radio contact.

LARK—Ladies' Amateur Radio Klub (Chicago, Ill.).

LASER—Light amplification by stimulated emission of radiation (developed at Hughes, 1960).

LASL—Los Alamos Scientific Laboratory.

LASO—Low-altitude search option.

LASS—Line amplifier and super sync mixer.

LASSO—Landing and approach system, spiral-oriented. Light aviation special support operations.

LAT—Latitude.

LAW—Light antitank weapon. Light area weapon (U.S. Army).

LAWSO—Lockheed Antisubmarine Warfare Systems Organization.

LB—Line buffer. Local battery.

LBE—Live better electrically.

LBO—Line building-out network (telephone term).

LC—Late commitment. Lead-covered cable. Level control. Library of Congress (Washington, D. C.). Line connector (telephone term). Line construction tool (JAN nomenclature). Link circuit. Load cell. Loud and clear.

LCAO—Linear combination of atomic orbitals.

LCARC—Lake County Amateur Radio Club (Gary, Ind.).

LCC—Landing craft, control. Launch control center. Launch control console.

LCCA—Load current contact aiding.

LCDTL—Load-compensated diode-transistor logic.

LCF—Launch control facility.

LCI—Landing craft, infantry.

LCL—Local.

LCM—Landing craft, medium. Least common multiple.

LCP—Landing craft, personnel.

LCP(L)—Landing craft, personnel (large).

LCP(N)—Landing craft, personnel (nested).

LCP(R)—Landing craft, personnel (ramp).

LCR—Inductance-capacitance-resistance. Landing craft, rubber.

LCRE—Lithium-cooled reactor experiment.

LCS—Land combat system. Landing craft, support. Liaison call sheet. Line coding storage. Loudness contour selector.

LCSS—Launch control and sequencer system.

LCT—Laboratoire Central de Telecommunications (French agency). Landing craft, tank. Launch control trailer.

LCVD—Least voltage coincidence detection.

LCVP—Landing craft, vehicle, personnel.

LCZR—Localizer.

LD—Lamp driver. Lethal dose (used in radiation study). Level discriminator. Light driver. Linear decision. Logic driver. Long distance. Low drag.

L/D—Lift to drag ratio.

LD-BLC—Low drag-boundary layer control.

LDC—Latitude data computer.

LDDS—Low-density data system.

LDE—Linear differential equations.

LDNA—Long-distance navigation aid.

LDR—Level distribution recorder. Light-dependent resistor. Low data rate.

LDRI—Low data rate input.

LDS—Liquid, diesel-cycle, supercharged.

LE—Leading edge. Low explosive.

LEAR—Logistics evaluation and review techniques.

LEAS—Lower echelon automatic switchboard.

LEB—London Electricity Board.

LECS—Launching equipment checkout set (developed by ITT for the BOMARC).

LEG—Logistics Evaluation Group.

LEL—Lower explosive limit.

LELTS—Lightweight electronic locating and tracking system.

LEM—Lunar excursion module (Project Apollo).

LEO—Lyon's Electronic Office (computer developed by J. Lyon & Co., Ltd., England; based on EDSAC).

LEP—Laboratoire d'Electronique et de Physique Appliqué (French agency).

LES—Lilliput Edison screw.

LESS—Lease cost estimating and scheduling.

LET—Linear energy transfer (stopping power-the energy loss per unit distance of penetration—used in radiation studies).

LF—Launch facility. Line feed. Line finder (teletype term). Low frequency.

LFBR—Liquid fluidized bed reactor (developed by The Martin Co.).

LFC—Laminar flow control. Low-frequency correction.

LFINT—Low-frequency intersection.

LFM—VHF fan-type marker (low powered-5 watts).

LF/MF—Low-frequency / medium-frequency four-course radio range.

LFQ—Light foot quantizer (time-measuring equipment manufactured by Computer Equipment Corp.).

LFR—Low flux reactor.

LG—Level gage. Liquid gas. Loop gain.

LGC—Lunar gas chromatograph.

LGN—Line gate number.

LGO—Lamont Geological Observatory.

LGR—Low group receiving unit.

LGT—Low group transmitting unit.

LH—Left-handed. Lithium sulfate (piezoelectric material).

L/H—Low-to-high.

LHA—Local hour angle.

LHCP—Left-hand circularly polarized.

LI—Level indicator. Lithographer (U. S. Navy).

LIBR—Library.

LICOF—Land lines communications facilities.

LIDAR—Light equivalent of radar.

LIEMC—Long Island Electronics Manufacturers' Council.

LIFE—Lear integrated flight equipment (a command instrument system manufactured by Lear, Inc.).

LIFMOP—Linearly frequency-modulated pulse.

LIL—Lunar International Laboratory.

LIM—Limit.

LINAC—Linear accelerator.

LINS—Lightweight inertial navigation system.

LIQ—Liquid.

LITR—Low-intensity test reactor (Oak Ridge, Tenn.).

L-I-W—Loss-in-weight.

LIWB—Livermore water boiler.

LL—Loudness level. Low-level. Lower limit.

LLFPB—Linear, lumped, finite, passive, bilateral (networks).

LLL—Low-level logic.

LLP—Lunar landing program.

LLPN—Lumped, linear, parametric network.

LLSV—Lunar logistic supply vehicle.

LLV—Lunar logistic vehicle.

lm—Lumen.

LMAFS—Lookout Mountain Air Force Station.

L/MF—Low and medium frequency.

LMFR—Liquid-metal-fuel reactor.

LMFRE—Liquid metal-fueled reactor experiment.

LMG—Liquid methane gas.

LMM—Compass locator station combined with middle marker of the ILS (FAA term).

LMO—Lens - modulated oscillator (klystron developed by Sperry Tube Division).

LO—Local oscillator. Locked-oscillator.

LOB—Launch operations building (missile term). Line of balance.

LOBAR—Long baseline radar (for missile detection—ITT Labs, Nutley, N. J.).

LOC—Launch operations center. Lines of communication.

LOCO—Long cores (project similar to "Mohole").

LOCS—Librascope operations control system.

LOCTRACS—Lockheed tracking

and control system.

LOD—Launch Operations Directorate (NASA).

LODAR—Technique similar to radar, but signal is transmitted in water at supersonic frequencies.

LODESTAR—Logically organized data entry, storage and recording (developed by Argonne National Laboratory).

LOFAR—Low-frequency acquisition and ranging.

LOFTI—Low-frequency trans-ionospheric satellite.

LOG—Logarithm.

LOGANDS—Logical commands.

LOGIPAC—Logical processor and computer.

LOGLAN—Logical language.

LOGRAM—Logical program.

LOH—Light observation helicopter.

LOM—Locator outer marker (compass locator, when installed as outer marker site or within 5.5 miles of middle marker—FAA term).

LOP—Line of position.

LOPAIR—Long path infrared.

LOPO—Low-power water boiler (reactor) (Los Alamos, N. Mex.).

LOPPLAR—Laser doppler radar.

LO-QG—Locked oscillator - quadrature grid.

LOR—Lunar orbit rendezvous.

LORAC—Long-range accuracy (distance measuring system developed by Seiscor Div. of Seismograph Service Co.).

LORAD—Long-range active detection (sonar system).

LORAN—Long-range navigation.

LOREC—Long-range earth current communications system (developed by Space Electronics Corp.).

LORV—Low-observability reentry vehicle (U. S. Air Force Ballistic Systems Division project).

LOS—Line of sight. Loss of signal.

LOTS—Logistics over the shore.

LOZ—Liquid ozone.

LP—Leaving places. Linear programming. Long-playing (phonograph record). Low pass. Low pressure.

LPARM—Liquid-propellant applied research motor.

LPC—Linear power controller.

LPD—Log-periodic dipole.

LPDA—Log-periodic dipole array.

LPF—Logically passive function. Low-pass filter.

LPG—Liquid petroleum gas. Liquid propane gas.

LPG-30—Librascope General Precision Model 30 general-purpose digital computer (marketed by Royal McBee).

LPHB—Low-pressure heating boiler.

LPIA—Liquid Propellant Information Agency (operated by the Applied Physics Laboratory, John Hopkins University).

LPR—Late position report. Liquid-propellant rocket. Looper position regulator.

LPSD—Logically passive self-dual.

LPTF—Low-power test facility.

LPV—Log-periodic V antenna.

lpw—Lumens per watt.

LQT—Linear quantizer.

LR—Level recorder. Line relay. Liquid rocket.

LRBM—Long-range ballistic missile.

LRC—Langley Research Center (NASA, Langley Field, Va.). Level-recording controller.

LRCO—Limited radiocommunication outlet.

LRD—Long-range data.

LRE—Liquid rocket engine.

LRG—Long range.

LRI—Long-range radar input.

LRIM—Long-range input monitor.

LRIR—Low-resolution infrared radiometer.

LRL—Lawrence Radiation Facility

(Atomic Energy Commission installation).

LRLM—Lower reject limit median. Long-range missile launcher.

LRP—Long-range plans.

LRR—Long-range radar.

LRS—Long-range search. Long right shift.

LRWE—Long-range weapons establishment (joint British-Australian missile range at Woomera, Australia).

LS—Laser system. Late scramble. Level switch. Light source. Limit switch (JIC and NMTBA term). Line stretcher. Loudspeaker (JAN nomenclature).

LSB—Launch service buildings (missile term). Least significant bit. Lower sideband.

LSC—Limit - signaling comparator (manufactured by RCA). Liquid scintillation counter.

LSD—Landing ship dock. Low-speed data.

LSE—Lunar support equipment.

LSHV—Laminated synthetic high voltage (cable term).

LSLA—Lower specification limit for average of acceptable lots.

LSM—Landing ship, medium (U. S. Navy). Logistic support manager.

LSM(R)—Landing ship, medium—rocket (U. S. Navy).

LSN—Line - stabilization network. Linear sequential network.

LSO—Landing signal officer. Launch safety officer.

LSP—Low-speed printer.

LSR—Large ship reactor.

LSS—Life-saving ship. Life-support system.

LST—Landing ship, tank (U. S. Navy). Local sidereal time.

LST-G—Large steam turbine-generator.

LSV—Landing ship, vehicle (U.S. Navy).

LT—Indicating light (JIC term). Laminated teflon tape. Level trigger. Low-temperature noncontaminating jacket (wire and cable). Lug terminals. Transportation.

LTA—Lighter than air.

LTC—Load tap changing (autotransformers).

LTD-STD—Limited standard.

LTHA—Long-term heat aging.

LTM—Line type modulator.

LTP—Lower trip point.

LTPD—Lot tolerance percent defective.

LTV—Long tube vertical.

LU—Line unit (telephone term). Load unit.

LUF—Lowest usable frequency.

LUHF—Lowest usable high frequency.

LULU—Airborne nuclear depth charge.

LUT—Launch umbilical tower.

LV—Low-voltage.

LVCP(H)—Hydrofoil landing craft (U. S. Navy).

LVDS—Liquid, vee, diesel-cycle, supercharged.

LVEA—Lehigh Valley Electronic Association.

LVH—Landing vehicle hydrofoil.

LVN—Low-voltage neon.

LVOR—Low-power VOR.

LVP—Light valve projector.

LVST—Longitudinal velocity sorter tube.

LVT—Landing vehicle, tracked (amphibious landing vehicle used by Marine Corps; can be directed by radio from a hovering helicopter). Linear velocity transducer.

LW—Light wall. Long-wave.

LWC—Liquid water content.

LWD—Larger word.

LWL—Low water line.

LWM—Low water mark.

LWR—Lower.

lx—Lux.

LYR—Layer.

M

M—Crossed-field device. Figure of merit (tubes). Mach number. Magnetic. Magnetron. Medium. Medium-power. Mega- (prefix: 1 million or 10^6). Meter. Microphone (JAN nomenclature). Missile (Air Force vehicle designation). Mobile. Monitor (scan and alarm). Motor. Motor starter contactor (JIC term). Multiple launch (Air Force defense). Mylar.

m—milli- (prefix: 0.001 or 10^{-3}).

MA—Magnesium Association (122 E. 42nd St., New York 17, N.Y.). Magnetic amplifier. Mechanical advantage. Mechano-acoustic. Memory address. Microalloy. Military attache.

MA-1—Mercury astronaut 1 (first production capsule for project Mercury—developed by McDonnell Aircraft).

MAAG—Military Assistance Advisory Group.

MAAM—Medium antiaircraft missile.

MAB—Missile assembly building.

MABLE—Miniature autonetics baseline equipment (gyrocompass developed by Autonetics for U.S. Army).

MAC—McLeod aerating cardiac (pump). Maximum allowable concentration. Motion-analysis camera.

MACCS—Manufacturing and cost-control system.

MACE—Massachusetts Association of Consulting Engineers.

MACS — McDonnell automatic checkout system (used for the F-101 Voodoo). Missile air-conditioning system. Multiple-application connector system.

MAD—Magnetic airborne detector. Magnetic anomaly detection. Maintenance and disassembly. Michigan algorithm decoder. Motor assembly and disassembly. Multiaperture devices. Multiply and add.

MADALINE—Many adaptive linear classification machines.

MADDAM—Macromodule and digital differential analyzer machine (developed by Burroughs Corp.).

MADDIDA—Magnetic-drum digital differential analyzer.

MADE—Microalloy diffused electrode. Minimum airborne digital equipment. Multichannel analog-to-digital data encoder (developed by General Mills).

MADIS—Millivolt analog-digital instrumentation system (developed by Arnoux Corp., Los Angeles, Calif.).

MADRAC—Malfunction detection and recording.

MADRE—Magnetic-drum receiving equipment (developed by Naval Research Lab). Martin automatic data-reduction equipment system (developed by The Martin Co.).

MADT—Microalloy diffused-base transistor.

MAECON—Mid-America Electronics Convention.

MAF—Mixed amine fuel (rocket propellant).

MAFB—Mitchell Air Force Base.

MAFD—Minimum acquisition flux density (infrared detector term).

MAFL—Multiaperture ferrite logic.

MAG—Magnetic. Magnetron. Marine Aircraft Group. Military Advisory Group.

MAGI—Multi-array gamma irradiator (developed by Curtiss-Wright).

MAGNOX—Magnesium oxide.

MAJAC—Monitor, antijam, and control console.

MALLAR—Manned lunar landing and return.

MAMI—Machine-aided manufacturing information.

MAMS—Modern army maintenance system.

MAN—Microwave aerospace navigation (developed by Sperry Phoenix Co., division of Sperry Rand). Modern army needs.

MANOP—Manual of operation.

MANTRAC—Manual angle-tracking capability (developed by Boeing).

MAP—Message - acceptance pulse. Michigan Association of Professions. Military assistance programs. Multiple array processor. Mutual aid program.

MAPCHE—Mobile automatic programmed checkout equipment.

MAPI—Machinery and Allied Products Institute.

MAR—Memory address register.

MARAD—Maritime Administration experimental hydrofoil.

MARC—Moore automatic remote control.

MARCOMP—Martin dynamic computer chassis analyzer.

MARI—Motivator and response indicator.

MARS—Magnetic airborne recording system. Manned astronautical research station (developed by General Dynamics, San Diego, Calif.). Martin automatic reporting system. Master attitude reference system (Air Force project). Military affiliate radio systems. Miniature attitude reference system (developed by Whittaker Div., Telecomputing Corp. — Los Angeles, Calif.). Mobile Atlantic range station (instrumented tracking ship). Multiaperture reluctance switch.

MART—Mobile automatic radiation tester (developed by Hughes Aircraft Co.).

MARTAC—Martin automatic rapid test and control (developed by The Martin Co., Denver, Colo.).

MARTEC—Martin thin-film electronic circuit.

MARTINI—Massive analog recording technical instrument for nebulous indications (manufactured by Hewlett-Packard).

MARVEL—Mississippi aerophysics research vehicle with extended latitude.

MAS—Military Agency for Standardization (department of NATO). Missile alinement set. Milliampere-seconds (radiology term).

MASCOT—Motorola automatic sequential computer-operated tester.

MASER—Microwave amplification by stimulated emission of radiation.

MASK—Maneuvering and Seakeeping Facility (installation at David Taylor Model Basin).

MASSDAR — Modular analysis, speedup, sampling, and data reduction (developed by General Applied Science Laboratories, Inc.).

MAST—Magnetic annular shock tube (MHD device developed by AVCO). Missile automatic supply technique.

MASTIF—Multiple-Axis Test Inertial Facility (NASA, Lewis Re-search Center, Cleveland, Ohio).

MAT—Microalloy transistor.

MATCH—Multielement assured tracking chopper.

MATE—Modular automatic test equipment (manufactured by Associated Missile Products Co.).

MATS—Military Air Transport Service.

MATTS—Multiple airborne target trajectory system (all-weather tracking system manufactured by Cubic Corp.).

MATU—Marine air traffic unit.

MAUDE—Morse automatic decoder (developed by Lincoln Lab., Massachusetts Institute of Technology).

MAULT—Manual and/or automatic ultrasonic laboratory testing tank (developed by Elion Ultrasonics).

MAVAR—Mixer amplification by variable reactance.

MAW—Medium assault weapon (a 90-mm recoilless rifle manufactured by Firestone Tire and Rubber Co.).

MAXSECOM—Maximum security communications (infrared communications system developed by Minneapolis-Honeywell).

MB—Medium bombardment. Meltback. Memory buffer. Millibars.

M-B—Make-break.

MBB—Make-before-break.

MBC—Maximum breathing capacity (medical term). Miniature bayonet cap.

MBL—Miniature button light.

MBO—Meacham bridge oscillator. Monostable blocking oscillator.

MBST—Multiple beam - switching tube.

MBT—Main battle tank. Mercaptobenzothiazole.

MBTWR—Multiple-beam traveling-wave klystron.

MBV—Minimum breakdown voltage.

MBWO—M-type backward-wave oscillator.

MC—Magnetic clutch (JIC and NMTBA term). Marine Corps. Maritime Commission. Master control.

MCA—Microminiature Components Advisory Committee (Electronics Industries Association).

MCAS—Marine Corps Air Station.

MCAT—Midwest Council on Airborne Television.

MCC—Main communications centers. Mercury control center. Miniature center cap. Miscellaneous common carrier. Modulation with constant coefficient. Multicomponent circuits.

MCEB—Military Communications Electronics Board.

MCEU—Mobile Civil Emergency Unit (an organization of Citizens band radio operators, 1203 Butternut St., Syracuse, N.Y.).

MCF—Multichannel, fixed (telephone term).

MCGS—Microwave command guidance system (developed by Sperry Phoenix Co.).

MCL—Mid-Canada line. Miniature cartridge light.

MCM—Thousand circular mils.

MCO—Marine Corps Officer.

MCOP—Multiple-conductor, oil-resistant, portable, synthetic-insulation cable.

MCOT—Missile checkout trailer.

MCP—Master control program.

MCR—Master control routine. Military compact reactor (developed by Allison Div., General Motors Corp.).

MCS—Master control system. Microwave carrier supply. Mine countermeasure support ship (U.S. Navy). Motor circuit switch (JIC and NMTBA term). Multipurpose

communications and signaling.

MCT—Movable-core transformer.

MCU—Miniature command unit.

MCW—Modulated continuous wave.

MCX—Minimum-cost estimating.

MD—Medium-duty. Message data. Microalloy diffused. Motor drive.

M-D—Modulation-demodulation.

MDAP—Mutual Defense Assistance Program.

MDC—Missile development center. Mobile distress calling.

MDCT—Multidimensional compensatory task.

MDD—Median droplet diameter.

MDF—Main distributing frame. Medium-frequency direction finding. Mild detonating fuze.

MDFNA—Maximum-density fuming nitric acid (rocket fuel).

MDGL—Multiple - conductor, degaussing, lead-covered conductor.

MDI—Miss-distance indicator. Multiple-display indicator.

MDL—Miniature display light.

MDLC—Materiel Development and Logistic Command (U.S. Army).

MDMS — Miss - distance measuring system (developed by Aircraft Armaments Co.).

MDNA—Machinery Dealers' National Association. Maximum-density nitric acid (rocket fuel).

MDR—Master-clock generator. Multichannel data recorder.

MDS—Malfunction detection system. Master drum sender. Meteoroid-detection satellite. Minimum discernible signal.

MDT—Mean down time.

MDW—Multipair distribution wire.

ME—Measuring element. Mechanical efficiency. Microelectronic. Molecular electronics.

MEA—Minimum enroute IFR altitude.

MEAR—Maintenance engineering analysis records (U.S.   **[Cont.]**

Navy maintainability records).

MEB—Midlands Electricity Board (British electrical power agency).

MEC—Manufacturing Engineering Council.

MECA—Maintainable electronic component assembly. Multielement component arrays.

MEDAL—Micro - mechanized data for automated logistics.

MEDIA—Magnavox electronic data image apparatus (developed by Magnavox Corp.).

MED-I-MON—Medical intensive-care monitor.

MEDIS—Message - diversion relay system (teletypewriter term).

MEDLARS—Medical literature analysis and retrieval system (National Library of Medicine, Washington, D.C.).

MEDUSA—Multiple-element directional universally steerable antenna.

MEE—Mechanical evaluation equipment.

MEETAT—Major improvement in electronic effectiveness through application of advanced techniques (U.S. Navy Bureau of Naval Weapons program).

MEG—Miniature electrostatic gyro.

MELVA—Military electronic light valve.

MEM—Mars excursion module.

MENEX—Maintenance Engineering Exchange Bulletin.

MENS—Microcell electronic weighing system.

MEP—Mean effective pressure.

MER—Minimum energy requirements.

MES—Miniature Edison screw.

MESUCORA—Association for Measurement, Control, Regulation, and Automation (40 Rue du Colisee, Paris 8e, France).

MET—Meteorological.

META—Metropolitan Educational Television Association (Toronto, Canada).

METOF—Meteorological office.

MET/SAT—Meteorolgoical satellite.

MeV—Million electron volts.

MEW—Microwave early warning.

MEX—Military exchange.

MF—Medium frequency. Microcard Foundation (901 26th St. N.W., Washington, D.C.). Multifrequency.

MFC—Magnetic-tape field scan. Micro-functional circuit.

MFD—Magnetic frequency detector.

MFED—Maximally flat envelope delay.

MFKP—Multifrequency key pulsing.

MFM—Magneto fluid mechanic. Maximally flat magnitude. Micrometer frequency meter.

MFP—Mixed fission products.

MFS—Magnetic-tape field search. Malleable Founders' Society (781 Union Commerce Bldg., Cleveland 14, Ohio). Military flight service.

MFSK—Multiple frequency - shift keying.

MFSO—Missile flight safety officer.

MFT—1000 feet. Polyester tape.

MftL—Milli-foot—lamberts.

MFVD—Maximum forward voltage drop.

MG—Laminated mylar tape and glass braid lacquered. Major general. Military governor. Motor-generator.

MGAP—Magnetic attitude prediction.

MGC—Missile - guidance computer (developed by IBM for Titan missile).

MGCR—Maritime gas-cooled reactor (a General Dynamics project).

MGD—Magneto gas dynamic. Million gallons per day.

MGE—Maintenance ground equipment.

MGN—Manganin.

MgO-RAD—Magnesium oxide radiation detector.

MGSA—General Military Supply Agency.

MH—Nondirectional radio homing beacon (50 watts or less).

MHD — Magnetohydrodynamics. Medium hard-drawn copper wire.

MHF—Mixed hydrazine fuel.

MHFF—Multiple - conductor, heat and flame-resistant, flexible synthetic resin and felted asbestos insulation.

MHI—Material Handling Institute.

MHIA—Mobile, high-powered operational plant number one (floating atomic power plant for Strategic Army Corps.).

MI—Malleable iron. Military intelligence. Mineral-insulated cable.

MIA—Metal interface amplifier (thin-film device, developed by Philco). Mouse-in-Able.

MIC—Michigan instructional computer. Microwave interference coordination.

MICR—Magnetic ink character recognition.

MICRAM—Microminiature individual components reliable assembled modules (U. S. Army program developed by Sylvania Lighting Products Div.).

MICROACE—Microminiature automatic checkout equipment (developed by Minneapolis-Honeywell, Aeronautical Div.).

MICROFIER—Microwave rectifier (developed by Raytheon Co.).

MI/DAC—Management information for decision-making and control.

MIDAR—Microwave detection and ranging.

MIDARM—Microdynamic angle and rate monitoring system (man-ufactured by Razdow Labs., Inc., Newark, N. J.).

MIDAS—Military defense alarm system. Miniature data acquisition system (physiological telemetry system developed by Unilectron, Inc.). Missile defense alarm satellite. Missile intercept data acquisition system (manufactured by Cubic Corp.).

MIDOP—Missile doppler.

MIDOT—Multiple interferometer determination of trajectory.

MIG—Metal-inert-gas. Miniature integrating gyroscope (developed by Minneapolis-Honeywell).

MIL—One thousandth of an inch.

MILA—Merritt Island launch area.

MIL-E-CON—Convention on Military Electronics (sponsored by IRE, PGME).

MILS—Missile-impact locating system.

MIMS—Modular isodrive memory series.

MIND—Magnetic integrator neuron duplicator (artificial neuron developed by Aeronutronic Div., Ford Motor Co.).

MINITAS—Miniature true airspeed computer (developed by Servomechanisms, Inc.).

MIN MC—Minimum material condition.

MINS—Miniature inertial navigation system (developed by Kearfott).

MINT—Material identification and new-item control techniques (U. S. Air Force project).

MIP—Microwave interference protection. Missile impact prediction.

MIPE—Modular information-processing equipment.

MIPIR—Missile precision instrumentation radar.

MIPS—Missile impact predictor set.

MIR—Memory-information register.

MIRACLE—Mokum industrial research automatic calculator for laboratory and engineering (developed by Royal Dutch Shell).

MIRAK—Minimum-rakete (a small liquid-rocket motor).

MIRAN—Missile ranging.

MIRED—Micro - reciprocal degrees (optical term for expressing color temperature).

MIRRER—Microwave identification railroad encoding reflector (developed by Transdata, Inc.).

MIRTRAK—Martin infrared tracker (developed by The Martin Co.).

MIS—Man in space.

MISA—Military Industrial Supply Agency (central defense purchasing agency, 700 Robbins Ave., Philadelphia, Pa.).

MISS—Man-in-space-soonest (Air Force program). Mobile instrumentation support system (developed by Electronic Specialty Co., for the Pershing Missile).

MIST—Minimum structure modules (developed by Tele-Dynamics Div., Arma Corp.).

MISTIC—Michigan State integral computer.

MISTRAM — Missile trajectory measurement system (developed by General Electric Co., for Air Force Missile Test Center, Cape Canaveral).

MITE—Miniaturized integrated telegraph equipment.

MITI—Ministry of International Trade and Industry (Japanese government bureau).

MITR—MIT research reactor.

MITTS—Mobile IGOR tracking telescope system.

MJR—Maintenance job requests.

MK—Manual clock. Microphone.

MKR—Marker radio beacon.

MKSA—Meter-kilogram-second-ampere (Giorgi system of units).

ML—Machine language. Mine locomotive cable. Mission life (reliability term).

mL—Millilamberts.

MLC—Motor load control.

MLE—Maximum likelihood estimate.

MLI—Marker light indicator.

MLL—Manned lunar launching.

MLLP—Manned lunar landing program.

MLR—Mulitply and round.

MLT—Mass-loaded transducer. Microlayer transistor.

MLTY—Military.

MLY—Multiply.

MM—Machinist's mate (U. S. Navy). Main memory. Maritime mobile. Master monitor. Middle marker (instrument landing system). Missile master (built by The Martin Co.). Moore-Mealy (logic nets). Motor magnet.

MMC—Maximum material condition. Maximum metal concept.

MMCT—Maritime mobile coastal (telegraphy).

MMD—Moving map display.

MMF—Magnetomotive force.

MMH—Monomethyl hydrazine (rocket propellant).

MMI—Mechanized manufacturing information.

MMKR—Middle marker (instrument landing system).

MMP—Maritime mobile phone. Multiplexed message processor.

MMPC—Maritime mobile phone coastal.

MMPDC—Maritime mobile phone distress and calling.

MMPR—Missile manufacturer's planning report.

MMRBM—Mobile medium - range ballistic missile.

MMSS—Manned maneuverable space system.

MMT—Maritime mobile telegraphy.

MMTC — Maritime mobile telegraphy calling.

MMTDC—Maritime mobile telegraph distress and calling.

MMV—Monostable multivibrator.

MN—Manual (JIC term). Mineman (U. S. Navy).

MNDG—Magnetic heading.

MNTR—Monitor.

MNWEB — Merseyside and North Wales Electricity Board (British electrical power agency).

MO—Memory operation.

MOA—Ministry of Aviation (British government agency). Music Operators of America.

MOAMA—Mobile air materiel area (U. S. Air Force, Mobile, Ala.).

MOBIDAC—Mobile data acquisition system.

MOBIDIC—Mobile digital computer (designed by Sylvania).

MOC—Master operational controller. Master operations control (Titan countdown monitor).

MOCOM—Mobile command (U. S. Army).

MODEM—Modulator-demodulator.

MODI—Modified distribution (mathematical programming term).

MODS—Manned orbital development station (U. S. Air Force project).

MOE — Measure of effectiveness (missile term—dollars per pound of payload in orbit).

MOHO—Mohorovicic discontinuity.

MOLE-E-COM—Molecularized digital computer (developed by Westinghouse).

MOLS—Magnetic-operated limit switch.

MOMAR—Modern mobile army.

MON—Mixed oxides of nitrogen (rocket fuel). Monitor.

MONECA—Motor network calculator.

MONOK—Monitor resumed normal operation.

MONOS—Monitor out of service.

MOOSE—Man out of space easiest.

MOP—Masers a ondes progressives (French term).

MOPB—Manually operated plotting board.

MOPTAR—Multiobject phase tracking and ranging (developed by Cubic Corp.). Multiple-object precision tracking and ranging.

MOR—Low-frequency omnidirectional range. Magneto-optical rotation.

MOREPS—Monitor station reports.

MORT—Missile operation readiness testing.

MOS — Manufacturing operations system (IBM data-processing system). Mechanical oblique sketcher. Metal-oxide-silicon. Military operation specialty. Ministry of Supply (British agency for research and standards).

MOSES—Multioccupant sealed environment simulator.

MOSS—Manned orbiting space station.

MOT—Motor (NMTBA term).

MOUSE—Minimum orbital unmanned satellite earth.

MOWS—Manned orbital weapons system.

MP—Maintenance point. Manual pulser. Mathematical programming. Mechanical part. Melting point.

MPA—Metal Powder Association.

MPATI—Midwest Program on Airborne Television Instruction.

MPC—Maximum permissible concentration. Mechanized production control. Multipath core. Multiprogram control.

95

MPCA—Metal Powder Core Association.

MPD—Magneto plasmadynamic. Maximum permissible dose. Military personnel division.

MPE—Maximum permissible exposure.

MPG—Microwave pulse generator.

MPH—Miles per hour.

MPIF—Metal Powder Industries Federation (60 E. 52nd St., New York 17, N. Y.).

MPL—Marine Physical Laboratory (Scripps Institution of Oceanography). Model parts list.

MPM—Magnetic phase modulator.

MPO—Maximum power output.

MPPA—Metal Powder Producers' Association.

MPR—Master power regulator. Music power rating.

MPS—Meters per second.

MPT—Mercury procedures trainer (Project Mercury). Missile preflight tester (for MACE missile).

MPTA—Mechanical Power Transmission Association.

MPTE—Multipurpose test equipment (developed by RCA for Army Ordnance).

MPX—Multiplex.

MPY—Multiply.

MR—Memory register. Mercury-Redstone. Military regulations. Milliroentgens.

MRA—Multiple recording accelerometer.

MRBM—Medium - range ballistic missile.

MRC—Magnetic rectifier control. Maximum reverse current. Micro-Research Corp. (c/o American Antiquarian Society, 185 Salisbury St., Worcester, Mass.).

MRDF—Maritime radio direction finding.

MRG—Medium range.

MRI—Monopulse resolution improvement.

MRIA—Magnetic Recording Industry Association.

MRIR—Medium-resolution infrared radiometer.

MRKD—Marked.

MRML — Medium - range missile launcher.

MRN—Maritime radio navigation.

MRO—Maintenance, repair and operating. Mechanized radar observer.

MRP—Maximum resolving power.

MRR—Medical research reactor (Upton, N. Y.).

MRS—Multipurpose research system.

MRSD—Maximum rated standard deviation.

MRSV—Maneuverable, recoverable space vehicle.

MRTM—Maritime.

MRTP—Military reliable tube program.

MRU—Machine records unit.

MRWC—Multiple reading and writing simultaneous with computing.

MS—Mean square. Memory system. Military secret. Military standard. Mirror or even symmetry.

Ms—Mesa.

MSA—Mine safety appliances. Mutual Security Agency.

MSAC—Moore School automatic computer (University of Pennsylvania).

MSB—Most significant bit.

MSC—Manned spacecraft center (NASA—Houston, Texas). Midwestern Simulation Council. Motor-starting contactor (NMTBA term).

MSCA—Multiple - conductor, shipboard, for control use, armored cable.

MSD—McNaney spectroelectric device (developed by Joseph T. Mc-

Naney). Method of steepest descent. Multifrequency signal detector.

MSE—Missile-support equipment.

MSFC—Marshall Space Flight Center (NASA—Huntsville, Ala.).

MSG—Message.

MSG/WTG—Message waiting.

MSL—Mean sea level.

MSMV—Monostable multivibrator.

MSO—Maintenance standard order.

MSPU—Multiple shielded pair, unarmored cable.

MSR—Magnetic shift register. Merchant ship, reactor (N. S. Savannah). Molten salt reactor.

MSS—Manufacturers' Standardization Society (valve and fittings industry). Meteorological Satellite Section (U. S. Weather Bureau).

MSSS—Manned static space simulator.

MST—Microsecond trip. Mobile service tower. Mobile strike term.

MSTS—Military Sea Transportation Service (U. S. Navy).

M-SV—Nonautomatic self-verification.

MT—Machine tool wire. Machine translation. Magnetic tape. Megaton. Meteorological aids. Metric ton. Mode transducer. Motor transport. Multiple transfer.

MTB—Maintenance of true bearing. Multichannel triple-bridge (temperature-measuring system developed by Rosemount Eng. Co.).

MTBF—Mean time between failures (reliability term).

MTC—Memory test computer.

M&TC—Mission and traffic control (U. S. Air Force term).

MTCA—Ministry of Transport and Civil Aviation (British).

MTCU—Magnetic tape control unit.

MTD—Mounted.

MTDS—Marines' tactical data system.

MTE—Maximum tracking error. Multi-system test equipment.

MTF — Mississippi Test Facility (NASA installation).

MTFD—Minimum tracking flux density (infrared detection term).

MTI—Metal Treating Institute. Moving target indicator.

MTR—Magnetic tape recorder. Materials testing reactor (Argonne National Laboratories). Military temperature range. Missile-tracking radar. Motor (JIC term). Multitrack range.

MTRL—Material.

MTS—Missile training squadron. Mobile-telephone service (telephone term).

MTSS—Manned test space station.

MTT—Magnetic tape terminal.

MTTR—Mean time to repair.

MTU—Multiplexer and terminal unit.

MU—Machine unit.

MUDPAC—Melbourne (Australia) University dual-package analog computer.

MUF—Maximum usable frequency.

MUL—Multiply.

MUPO — Maximum undistorted power output.

MURA—Midwest Universities Research Association.

MUSA—Multiple-unit steerable antenna.

MUV—Mobile underwater vehicle.

MUX—Multiplex.

MUX-ARQ — Multiplex-automatic error correction.

MV—Mean value. Measured value. Muzzle velocity.

MVAU—Maximum volt - ampere utilization.

MVBD—Multiple V-belt drive.

MVRTTG—Mohawk Valley Radio-TV Technicians' Guild.

MW—Manual word. Medium wall. Medium-wave.

MWD—Megawatt days. Molecular weight distribution.
MWD/T—Megawatt days per ton.
MWI—Message-waiting indicator.
MWO—Modification work order.

MWSC—Midwestern Simulation Council.
Mx—Maxwell.
MXR—Mask index register.

N

N—Avogadro's number. Counts (for radiation counter tubes). Natural number. Neoprene. Newton. Nichrome. No. Number of bits. Test (Air Force mission designation).
NA—National Army. Naval Aircraft. North America. Not assigned. Numerical aperture.
NAAFI—Navy, Army and Air Force Institute (British).
NAAS—Naval Auxiliary Air Station.
NAB—National Association of Broadcasters. Nut and bolt (tool designed by AMF).
NABET—National Association of Broadcast and Engineering Technicians.
NABUG—National Association of Broadcast Unions and Guilds (37 W. 46th St., New York 36, N. Y.).
NACARM—Northwestern American Civil Air Routes Manual.
NACC—National Automatic Controls Conference.
NACCAM—National Coordinating Committee for Aviation Meteorology.
NACE—National Association of Corrosion Engineers (1061 M & M Building, Houston, Texas).
NACOR—National Advisory Committee on Radiation (U. S. Public Health Service).
NACOS—National Communications Schedule.
NACR—National Advisory Com-

mittee on Radiation.
NAD—Naval Ammunition Depot.
NADAR—North American data airborne recorder.
NADC—Naval Air Development Center (Johnsville, Pa.).
NAEB—National Association of Educational Broadcasters (2500 Municipal Building, New York 7, N. Y.).
NAEC—National Aviation Education Council (1025 Connecticut Ave. N.W., Washington 6, D. C.).
NAECON—National Aeronautical Electronics Conference.
NAED—National Association of Electrical Distributors (290 Madison Ave., New York 17, N. Y.).
NAF—Naval Air Facility.
NAFEC—National Aviation Facilities Experimental Center (Federal Aviation Agency, Atlantic City, N. J.).
NAFI—Naval Avionics Facility, Indianapolis.
NAFLI—Natural flight.
NAIP—National Association of Industrial Plants, Inc. (Suite 604, 300 W. 43rd St., New York 36, N. Y.).
NAIR—Narrow absorption infrared.
NAM—National Association of Manufacturers.
NAMC—Naval Air Material Center (Philadelphia, Pa.).
NAMF—National Association of Metal Finishers.

NAMFI—NATO missile-firing installation.

NAMM—National Association of Music Merchants.

NAMPPF—Nautical air miles per pound of fuel.

NAMTRAGRU—Naval Air Maintenance Training Group.

NANAC—National Aircraft Noise Abatement Council.

NANEP—Navy Air Navigation Electronics Project (Patuxent, Md.).

NANWEP—Navy Numerical Weather Problems Group.

NAOS—North Atlantic ocean station.

NAP—Nuclear auxiliary power.

NAPA—National Association of Purchasing Agents. National Automotive Parts Association.

NAPE—National Association of Power Engineers.

NAPM—National Association of Photographic Manufacturers.

NAPU—Nuclear Auxiliary Power Unit.

NAQF—North Atlantic quality figures.

NAR—National Association of Rocketry.

NARAS—National Academy of Recording Arts and Sciences (P.O. Box 2671, Hollywood 28, Calif.).

NARBA—North American Regional Broadcasting Agreement.

NARC—Ninth Area Radio Club.

NARCOM—North Atlantic Relay Communication System.

NARDA—National Appliance and Radio-TV Dealers' Association.

NAREC—Naval Research Laboratory Electronic Digital Computer.

NARM—National Association of Relay Manufacturers.

NARS—Nonaffiliated reserve section.

NARTB—National Association of Radio and TV Broadcasters.

NARTS—Naval Air Rocket Test Station.

NAS—National Academy of Sciences. National Aircraft Standards. Naval Air Station.

NASA—National Aeronautics and Space Administration.

NASB—Navigational Aid Support Bases.

NASC—National Aeronautics and Space Council.

NASCO — National Academy of Sciences Committee on Oceanography.

NASM—Naval Aviation School of Medicine.

NASMO—NATO Starfighter Management Office.

NASRR—North American search and range radar (developed by North American Aviation).

NASS—National Aids Support System (Managed by Directorate of Materiel Management, Rome Air Materiel Area, Griffiss AFB, Rome, N. Y.).

NATC—National Air Taxi Conference. Naval Air Test Center (Patuxent River, Md.).

NATCC—National Air Transport Coordinating Committee.

NATESA—National Alliance of TV and Electronic Service Associations.

NATO—North Atlantic Treaty Organization.

NATOPS—U. S. Naval Air Training and Operating Procedures Standardization Program.

NATS—Naval Air Transport Service.

NAV—Navigation. Navigational.

NAVA—National Audio-Visual Association (Fairfax, Va.).

NAVAIDS—Navigational aids (operated by The Airways and Air Communications Service).

NAVBMC—Navy Ballistic Missile

Committee.

NAVDAC—Navigation data assimilation center (developed by Sperry for Polaris). Navigation data assimilation computer.

NAVPECO—Navy Production Equipment Control Office.

NAVTRADEVCEN — U. S. Navy Training Device Center.

NAW—National Association of Wholesalers.

NAWAS—National Attack Warning System.

NAWS—National Aviation Weather System.

NB—Narrow-band.

NBA—Narrow-band allocation.

NBAA—National Business Aircraft Association.

NBFAA—National Burglar and Fire Alarm Association.

NBFM—Narrow-band frequency modulation.

NBFU—National Board of Fire Underwriters (85 John St., New York, N. Y.).

NBR — Nonrebreathing (biomedical).

NBS—National Bureau of Standards.

NBSBL—National Bureau of Standards Boulder Laboratories (Boulder, Colo.).

NBTL—Naval Boiler and Turbine Laboratory.

NC—National Center (telephone term). Nickel-clad copper. No connection. Noise criterion. Nonlinear capacitance. Normally closed. Numerical control.

NCA—Northwest Computing Association.

NCAE—National Conference on Aeronautical Electronics.

NCAEI—National Conference on the application of electrical insulation.

NCAR—National Center for Atmospheric Research (Boulder, Colo.).

NCB—Naval Construction Battalion (Seebees—U. S. Navy).

NCEL—U. S. Naval Civil Engineering Laboratory (Port Hueneme, Calif.).

NCER—National Conference on Electromagnetic Relays.

NCFEA—North Carolina Federation of Electronic Associations.

NCI—National Cancer Institute (National Institutes of Health).

NCIH—National Conference on Industrial Hydraulics.

NCMT—Numerical controlled machine tool.

NCO—National Credit Office (official mercantile agency of the electronics industry).

NCRL—National Citizens Radio League (6272 W. North Ave., Chicago, Ill.).

NCRPM—National Committee on Radiation Protection and Measurement (sponsored by U. S. National Bureau of Standards).

NCS—Net control station.

NCSBEE—National Council of State Boards of Engineering Examiners.

NCSL—National Conference of Standards Laboratories.

NCTA—National Community Television Association, Inc.

NCTO—Naval Central Torpedo Office (Newport, R. I.).

NCU—Nozzle Control Unit.

NCUR—National Committee for Utilities Radio.

ND—No detect (telephone term). Non-discoloring.

NDB—Nondirectional beacon.

NDE—Nonlinear differential equations.

NDEA—National Defense Education Act.

NDRC—National Defense Research Committee.

NDRO—Nondestructive readout.

NDT—Nondestructive testing.

NDTA—National Defense Transportation Association.

NEAR—National emergency alarm repeater (OCDM home warning device produced by AC Spark Plug Div., GM, Flint, Mich.).

NEB—Noise equivalent bandwidth.

NEC—National Electrical Code. National Electronics Conference. Netherlands Electrotechnical Committee.

NEDA—National Electronic Distributors' Association. National Emergency Defense Airlift.

NEDECO—Netherlands Engineering Consultants.

NEEB—Northeastern Electricity Board (British electrical power agency).

NEEP—Nuclear Electronic Effects Program (Bell Labs research program).

NEES—Naval Engineering Experimental Station (Annapolis, Md.).

NEF—Noise equivalent flux.

NEFD—Noise equivalent flux density.

NEFO—National Electronics Facilities Organization.

NEI—Noise equivalent input. Noise equivalent intensity.

NEIPG—National Electronic Industries Procurement Group.

NEL—United States Naval Electronics Laboratory (San Diego, Calif.).

NELA—National Electric Light Association.

NELIAC—Navy Electronics Laboratory international algol compiler (dialect of algol).

NEMA—National Electrical Manufacturers' Association (155 E. 44th St., New York 17, N. Y.).

NEMAG—Negative effective mass amplifiers and generators.

NEP—Nearest equivalent product. New equipment practice. Noise equivalent power.

NEPA—Nuclear energy for propulsion of aircraft (U. S. Air Force Project at Oak Ridge, Tenn.).

NEP/CON—National Electronic Packaging and Production Conference.

NEPD—Noise equivalent power density.

NEPHS—Nephanalyses.

NER—Noise equivalent apparent target radiance difference.

NEREM—Northeast Electronics Research and Engineering Meeting (Boston, Mass.—held in November).

NERV—Nuclear emulsion recovery vehicle (General Electric NASA project).

NERVA—Nuclear engine for rocket vehicle application.

NES—Not elsewhere specified.

NESC—National Electrical Safety Code.

NET—National Educational Television. Noise equivalent temperature.

NETA—Northwest Electronic Technical Association (1233 S.E. 44th St., Portland 15, Ore.).

NETR—Nuclear engineering test reactor (U. S. Air Force).

NETRC—National Educational Television and Radio Center.

NEWS—Navy electronic warfare simulator.

NEXT—Near-end cross-talk loss.

NF—National formulary. Noise factor. Noise figure. Normal formula.

NFFS—Nonferrous Founders' Society.

NFPA—National Fire Protection Association (60 Battery March St., Boston 10, Mass.). National Fluid Power Association.

NFQ—Night frequency.

NFTW—National Federation of Telephone Workers.

101

NG—National Guard.

NGC—Near galactic catalog (astronomical term).

NGT—Noise generator tube.

NHI—National Heart Institute (National Institutes of Health).

NI—Noise index.

NIAC—National Industry Advisory Committee.

NIAID—National Institute of Allergy and Infectious Diseases (National Institutes of Health).

NIAMD—National Institute of Arthritic and Metabolic Diseases (National Institutes of Health).

NIB—Non-interference basis.

NIC—National Inventors' Council (U. S. Dept. of Commerce, Washington 25, D. C.). Negative-impedance converter. Nichrome.

NICAP—National Investigations Committee on Aerial Phenomena (1536 Connecticut Ave., Washington, D. C.).

NICB—National Industrial Conference Board.

NIDA—Numerically integrating differential analyzer.

NIDM—National Institute for Disaster Mobilization.

NIDR—National Institute of Dental Research (National Institutes of Health).

NIFTE—Neon indicator flashing test equipment (developed by Autonetics, Downey, Calif.).

NIH—National Institutes of Health (U. S. Public Health Service, Bethesda 14, Md.).

NIL—Nothing.

NIMA—National Insulation Manufacturers' Association (441 Lexington Ave., New York 17, N. Y.).

NIMH—National Institute of Mental Health (National Institutes of Health).

NINDB—National Institute of Neurological Diseases and Blindness

(National Institutes of Health).

NIPO—Negative input-positive output.

NIR—Near infrared.

NIRNS—National Institute for Research in Nuclear Science.

NIRPO—Naval Industrial Reserve Ordnance Plant (Naval installation for building missiles).

NISA—National Industrial Service Association, Inc. (now known as Electrical Apparatus Service Association, Inc.).

NJ—Nylon jacket extruded.

NJCC—National Joint Computer Committee.

NJSPE—New Jersey Society of Professional Engineers.

NL—Nylon braid lacquered.

NLE—Nonlinear element.

NLONTEVDET—New London Test and Evaluation Detachment.

NLPS—N-large energy gap, P-small energy gap (diode).

NLR—Noise load ratio. Nonlinear resistance.

NLRB—National Labor Relations Board.

NLS—No-load speed.

NM—Nautical miles. Nonmetallic-sheathed (cable). Not measured.

NMA—National Management Association. National Microfilm Association (P.O. Box 386, Annapolis, Md.).

NMAA—National Machine Accountants' Association.

NMC—National Meteorological Center. Nonmetallic sheathed cable, moisture- and corrosion-resistant. U. S. Naval Missile Center (Point Mugu, Calif.).

NMCC—National Military Command Center.

NMCS — National Military Command System (Defense communications agency).

NMDL—Navy Mine Defense Laboratory (Panama City, Fla.).

NME—National Military Establishment. Noise-measuring equipment.

NMEF—Naval Mine Engineering Facility (Yorktown, Va.).

NMF—Naval Missile Facility.

NMFPA—Naval Missile Facility, Point Arguello (Point Arguello, Calif.).

NMI—Nautical miles.

NMPS—Nautical miles per second.

NMR—Nuclear magnetic resonance.

NMRI—Naval Medical Research Institute (Bethesda, Md.).

NMRS—National Mobile Radio System.

NMTBA — National Machine Tool Builders' Association.

NNFP—Nuclear nitrogen fixation plant.

NNWH—Non-normal working hours.

NO—Normally open.

NOA—New obligational authority.

NOALA—Noise-operated automatic level adjustment (developed by Altec Lansing Corp.).

NODAC—Naval Ordnance Data Automation Center.

NODC—National Oceanographic Data Center (Washington, D. C.).

NOGL—Naval Ordnance Gage Laboratory (Naval Inspector's Office combined with WPSL).

NOHP—Not otherwise herein provided.

NOIBN—Not otherwise indexed by name.

NOL—Naval Ordnance Laboratory (Silver Spring, Md.).

NOLC—Naval Ordnance Laboratory, Corona, Calif.

NOL-MDI—Naval Ordnance Laboratory miss-distance indicator.

NOMAD—Navy oceanographic and meteorological automatic device.

NOMSS—National Operational Meteorological Satellite System.

NOMTF—Naval ordnance missile test facility.

NOO—Navy Oceanographic Office.

NOP—Naval Ordnance Plant (Forest Park, Ill.). No operation.

NORAC—No radio contacts.

NORAD—North American Air Defense Command.

NORC — National Oceanographic Records Center. Naval ordnance research calculator.

NORDO—No radio.

NOS—Not otherwise specified.

NOTAM—Notice to airmen.

NOTS—Naval Ordnance Test Station.

NP—Net proceeds. Nickel plate.

N_p—Neper.

NPA—Number plan area (telephone term).

NPD—Nuclear power demonstration (reactor, Des Joachims, Canada).

NPEF—New product evaluation form.

NPG—Naval Proving Grounds. Nuclear Power Group (group of midwestern utilities).

NPL—National Physical Laboratory (English agency similar to U. S. Bureau of Standards).

NPM—Counts per minute.

NPO—Navy Purchasing Office. Negative-positive-zero. Nuclear Propulsion Office (Joint NASA-AEC office, Germantown, Md.).

NPP—Naval Propellant Plant (Indian Head, Md.).

NPR—New production reactor. Noise power ratio (notch-to-notch ratio). Nuclear power reactor.

NPRFCA—National Petroleum Radio Frequency Coordinating Association.

NPS—Counts per second. Nominal pipe size.

NPSH—Net positive suction head.

NQR—Nuclear quadrupole [Cont.]

resonance.

NR—Natural rubber. Negative resistance. Nonlinear resistance. Number.

NRAB—Naval Reserve Air Base.

NRAC—Naval Research Advisory Committee.

NRAO—National Radio Astronomy Observatory (Greenbank, W. Va.).

NRB—Naval Reactors Board.

NRC — National Research Council. National Rocket Club.

NRD—Negative-resistance diode.

NRDL—U. S. Naval Radiological Defense Laboratory (San Francisco, Calif.).

NRDS—Nuclear Rocket Development Station (Jackson Flats area, AEC Nevada test site).

NRECA — National Rural Electric Cooperative Association.

NRF—Naval reactor facility. Naval repair facility.

NRL—Naval Research Lab.

NRM—Normalize.

NRMA—National Retail Merchants' Association.

NROE—Naval reactor organic experiment.

NROO—Naval Reactors Operations Office (Atomic Energy Commission installation at Schnectady, N. Y.).

NRPM—Nonregistered Publications Memoranda (U. S. Navy).

NRR—Naval research reactor.

NRRE—Netherlands Radar Research Establishment.

NRTS—Nuclear Reactor Testing Station (AEC — Idaho Falls, Idaho).

NRZ—Nonreturn to zero.

NRZ-C—Nonreturn-to-zero-change.

NRZ-M—Nonreturn-to-zero-mark.

NS—North-south. Not specified.

NSC—National Safety Council. National Security Council. National Space Council.

NSE—Nuclear support equipment.

nsec—Nanosecond.

NSF—National Science Fair. National Science Foundation.

NSFH—North-south fine, hundreds.

NSFT—North-south fine, tens.

NSFU—North-south fine, units.

NSIA—National Security Industrial Association.

NSMA—National Scale Men's Association (176 W. Adams St., Chicago 3, Ill.).

NSMPA—National Screw Machine Products Association.

NSMR—National Society for Medical Research (920 S. Michigan Ave., Chicago 5, Ill.).

NSP—Nonstandard part approval.

NSPE—National Society of Professional Engineers.

NSPL—N-small energy gap, P-large energy gap (diode).

NSRB—National Security Resources Board.

NSRC—National Stereophonic Radio Committee (Electronic Industries Association).

NSSCC—National Space Surveillance Control Center (Cambridge Research Center).

NSSP—National Severe Storms Project (U.S. Weather Bureau).

NST—Nonstaining.

NSTV—National Symposium on Vacuum Technology (sponsored by American Vacuum Society).

NT—Nit. No transmission. Numbering transmitter (teletype term).

NTA—Nuclear test airplane.

NTC—National Telemetering Conference.

NTCC—Nimbus Technical Control Center.

NTDC—Naval Training Device Center (Dept. of Office of Naval Research).

NTDMA—National Tool and Die Manufacturers' Association (907

Public Square Bldg., Cleveland 13, Ohio).

NTDPMA—National Tool, Die, and Precision Machining Association.

NTDS—Naval tactical data system (developed by Remington Rand).

NTFC—National TV Film Council (1501 Broadway, New York 36, N. Y.).

NTG—Nachrichtentechnische Gesellschaft (Telecommunications Engineering Society—Division of VDE, Association of German Electrical Engineers).

NTI — Noise transmission impairment.

NTP—Normal temperature and pressure.

NTS—Naval Training Station. Nevada Test Site (AEC Nuclear rocket test cells).

NTSC—National Television Systems Committee.

NTV—Nippon TV Network Corp.

NTX—Naval Communications System.

NTZ—North Temperate Zone.

NUDETS—Nuclear Detection and Reporting System.

NULACE—Nuclear liquid air cycle engine.

NULOR—Neuron locating and ranging.

NUMAR—Nuclear magnetic resonance.

NUPAD—Nuclear-powered active detection.

NUSL—Navy Underwater Sound Laboratory (Fort Trumbull, New London, Conn.).

NUSRL—Naval Underwater Sound Reference Laboratory (Dept. of Office of Naval Research).

nv—Neutron flux: Neutrons times velocity (unit of nuclear energy).

NVPA—National Visual Presentation Association.

NVPO—Nuclear Vehicle Projects Office.

nvt—Integrated (total) neutron flux (unit of nuclear energy).

NWA—Naval Weapons Annex.

NWAHACA—National Warm-Air Heating and Air Conditioining Association.

NWEB—Northwestern Electricty Board (British electrical power agency).

NWH—Normal working hours.

NWL—Naval Weapons Laboratory (Naval Facility, Dahlgren, Va.).

NWRC—Naval Weapons Research Center.

NWS—Naval Weapons Station.

NWSC—National Weather Satellite Center.

NYARTCC—New York Air Route Traffic Control Center.

NYSACE—New York State Association of Consulting Engineers.

NYSF—National Youth Science Foundation.

NYSSPE—New York State Society of Professional Engineers.

NZE—North-Zenith-East System.

O

O—Non-crossed-field device (from French "ordinaire"). Output.

OA—Office of the Administrator. Operations analyst.

OABETA—Office Appliance and Business Equipment Trades Association.

OAC—Oceanic Area Con-　**[Cont.]**

trol Centre (British air traffic control at Redbrae, Aryshire).

OAIDE—Operational assistance, and instructive, data equipment (manufactured by Lear).

OAO—Orbiting Astronomical Observatory.

OAPC—Office of Alien Property Custodian.

OAPM—Optimal amplitude and phase modulation.

OAR—Office of Aerospace Research (U.S. Air Force). Optical Automatic Ranging (developed by Comapco, Inc., 17071 Ventura Blvd., Encino, Calif.).

OARAC—Office of Air Research automatic computer.

OARC—Office of Air Research automatic calculator (designed and built for U. S. Air Force by General Electric).

OART—Office of Advanced Research and Technology (division of NASA).

OAS—Organization of American States.

OASR—Office of Aeronautical and Space Research (NASA).

OAT—Operating ambient temperature.

OATC—Oceanic air traffic control.

OBD—Omni-bearing distance.

OBE—Office of Business Economics. (U.S. Department of Commerce).

OBI—Omni-bearing indicator.

OBS—Omni-bearing selector.

OBSTN—Obstruction.

OC—Occurs. Office of Controls. Officer commanding. On course. Operating characteristic. Operating coil. Operations conductor. Outlet contact.

O/C—Open-circuit.

O & C—Operations and checkout.

OCC—Operations Control Center.

OCCA—Overseas Communications Cooperation Association.

OCCWS—Office of the Chief of Chemical Warfare Service.

OCDM—Office of Civil and Defense Mobilization.

OCDRE—Organic-cooled, heavy-water moderated reactor.

OCNO—Office of the Chief of Naval Operations (Main Navy Bldg., Washington 25, D.C.).

OCO—Office of the Chief of Ordnance.

OConUS—Outside continental United States.

OCR—Optical character recognition.

OCRD—Office of Chief of Research and Development (U.S. Army).

OCRE—Gas-cooled reactor experiment.

OCS—Office of Cataloguing and Standardization. Officer Candidate School.

OCSO—Office of the Chief Signal Officer (U.S. Signal Corps).

OCT—Octal.

OCTL—Open-circuited transmission line.

OD—Officer of the Day. Ordnance Department.

ODA-HCL—Octadecylamine hydrochloride (used for monolayer to reduce wear and friction).

ODD—Operator distance dialing (telephone term).

ODDRE—Office of the Director of Defense Research and Engineering (Washington, D.C.).

ODM—Office of Defense Mobilization.

ODP—Operational development program.

ODR—Office of Director of Defense Research. Omnidirectional range.

ODRE—Office of Defense Research and Engineering.

OE—Omissions excepted.

Oe—Oersted.

OECD—Organization for Economic

Cooperation and Development.

OEEC—Organization for European Economic Cooperation (Publications Office: 1346 Connecticut Ave., N.W., Washington 6, D.C.).

OEG—Operations Evaluation Group.

OEMI—Office Equipment Manufacturers' Institute.

OEP—Office of Emergency Planning.

OEPS—Office of Educational Programs and Services (division of NASA).

OF—Operational fixed.

O/F—Oxidant to fuel weight flow ratio.

OFACS—Overseas-foreign aeronautical communications station.

OFARS—Overseas-foreign aeronautical receiver station.

OFATS—Overseas-foreign aeronautical transmitter station.

OFHC—Oxygen-free, high-conductivity (grade of electrolytic copper).

OFMC—Operational Fixed Microwave Council (Association of American Railroads).

OFT—Operational flight trainer.

OG—Officer of the Guard. Or gate.

OGE—Operating ground equipment.

OGI—Outer grid injection.

OGL—Outgoing line.

OGM—Office of Guided Missiles (superseded by ARPA). Optimum gradient method.

OGMS—Ordnance Guided Missile School.

OGO—Orbiting geophysical observatory.

OGS—Outgoing secondary switches (telephone term).

OH—Ohmic heating,

OHTS—Oil hardening tool steel.

OIC—Officer in Charge.

OIG—Officer of the Inspector General.

OINC—Officer in charge.

OINT—Omni intersection.

OITT—Outpulser, identifier, trunk test (telephone term).

OJAG—Office of Judge Advocate General.

OKEC—European Economic Cooperation Organization (Paris, France).

OKI-TAC—Oki transistorized computer (developed by Oki Electric Industry Co., Ltd., Japan).

OL—Overlap (telephone term). Overload relay (JIC and NMTBA term).

O/L—Operations/logistics.

OLC—Outgoing line circuit (teletype term).

OLF—Orbital launch facility.

OLO—Orbital launch operation.

OLV—Orbital launch vehicle.

OM—Old man. Operational maintenance. Opticalman (U.S. Navy). Outer marker.

OMCR—Organic-moderated cooled reactor.

OMEC—Optimized microminiature electronic circuit.

OMFBR—Organic-moderated fluidized bed reactor.

OMGUS—Office of Military Government, United States.

OMKR—Outer marker (instrument landing system).

OMRE—Organic-moderated reactor experiment (at Nuclear Reactor Testing Station in Idaho).

OMSF—Office of Manned Space Flight (NASA).

OMTS—Organizational maintenance test station.

ONERA—Office Nationale d'Etudes et de Recherches Aeronautiques (French agency).

ONI—Office of Naval Intelligence.

ONR—Office of Naval Research.

OO—Ordnance Officer.

OOAMA—Ogden Air Materiel Area (Air Force depot, Ogden, Utah).

107

OOC—Organized Occupational Curricula.

OOD—Officer of the Deck (U.S. Navy).

OOPS—Off-line operating simulator (developed by General Electric).

OP—Observation post.

OPAL—Optical platform alignment linkage.

OPCON—Operating and control system (developed by Datatrol Corp., Silver Spring, Md.). Optimizing control (manufactured by Westinghouse).

OPD—Operations Division.

OpDevFor—Operational Test and Evaluation Force (successor to Operational Development Force—U.S. Navy, Norfolk, Va.).

OPEP—Orbital plane experimental package.

OPERG—Operating.

OPI—Office of Public Information (NASA). Oil pressure indicator.

OPIM—Order processing and inventory monitoring.

OPM—Operator programming method (Automatic programming system devised by Prof. A. A. Ljapunov of Moscow University, USSR).

OPNAV—Office of the Chief of Naval Operations.

OPPE—Office of Program Planning and Evaluation (NASA).

OPR—Operator tie-line.

OPS—Oblique photo sketcher.

OPT—Operate.

OPTAG—Optical pickoff two-axis gyro (developed by Perkin-Elmer Corp.).

OPTAR—Optical automatic ranging.

OpTevFor—Operational Test and Evaluation Force.

OPTUL—Optical pulse transmitter using laser.

OPV—Ohms per volt (British abbreviation).

OQI—Oil quantity indicator.

OQL—Observed quality level.

OQMG—Office of the Quartermaster General.

OR—Omnidirectional radio range. Operations research. Operations room. Order register. Or gate.

O/R—On request.

ORACLE—Oak Ridge automatic computer and logical engine.

ORB—Owner's risk of breakage.

ORBIT—Oak Ridge binary internal-translator.

ORBS—Orbiting rendezvous base system.

ORC—Officers' Reserve Corps. Operational readiness check.

ORCON—Organic control (U.S. Naval Research Lab project in which pigeons were used to guide missiles).

ORD—Optical rotary dispersion. Owner's risk of damage.

ORDALT—Ordnance alteration.

ORDRAT—Ordnance dial reader and translator.

ORF—Owner's risk of fire (or freezing).

ORG—Origin.

ORGPHC—Orographic.

ORI—Operational readiness inspection.

ORIC—Oak Ridge isochronous cyclotron.

ORINS—Oak Ridge Institute of Nuclear Studies (Oak Ridge, Tenn.).

ORL—Owner's risk of leakage.

ORNL—Oak Ridge National Laboratory (Atomic Energy Commission).

ORP—Oxidation-reduction potential.

ORR—Oak Ridge Research Reactor.

ORS—Operational Research Society (United Kingdom). Over range station. Owner's risk of shifting.

ORSA—Operations Research Society

of America.

ORSORT—Oak Ridge School of Reactor Technology.

ORUS—Official Register of the United States.

OS—Odd symmetric. One-shot multivibrator. Operator's set (telephone term). Ordinary seaman.

OSA—Optical Society of America (1155 16th St. N.W., Washington 6, D.C.).

OSCAR—Orbiting satellite carrying amateur radio.

OSD—Office of the Secretary of Defense.

OSDBMC—Office of the Secretary of Defense Ballistic Missile Committee.

OSF—Odd side flat.

OSFD—Office of Space Flight Development (NASA).

OSG—Office of the Surgeon General.

OSIS—Office of Scientific Information Service (National Science Foundation, 1951 Constitution Ave. N.W., Washington 25, D.C.).

OSL—Orbiting space laboratory.

OSM—Oxygen steelmaking.

OSO—Orbiting Solar Observatory.

OSP—Office of Surplus Property.

OSPE—Ohio Society of Professional Engineers.

OSR—Operational support requirement.

OSRD—Office of Scientific Research and Development.

OSRMD—Office of Scientific Research, Mechanics Division (U.S. Air Force).

OSS—Office of Space Sciences (NASA). Office of Strategic Services.

OSSigO—Office of the Chief Signal Officer.

OST—Office of Science and Technology (U.S. government commission).

OSTF—Operational silo test facility. Operational suitability test facility. Operational systems test facility.

OSTIV—Organization Scientifique et Technique Internationale du Vol a Voile.

OSURF—Ohio State University Research Foundation.

OSURO—Ohio State University Radio Observatory.

OSV—Ocean station vessel (North Atlantic weather ship).

OSW—Office of Saline Water (U.S. Department of Interior). Office of The Secretary of War.

OS & Y—Outside screw and yoke.

OT—Overtime.

OTAC—Ordnance Tank — Automatic Command (Detroit Arsenal—Center Line, Mich.).

OTC—Office of Transport and Communications. Oregon Technical Council.

OTL—Output-transformerless (type of amplifier).

OTR—Observed average temperature rise.

OTS—Office of Technical Services.

OTSA—Oregon Television Service Association (219 N. Evans St., McMinnville, Ore.).

OTU—Operational Training Unit.

OTUS—Office of The Treasurer of the United States.

OTVSA—Oregon TV Service Association.

OUSW—Office of the Undersecretary of War.

OUT—Output.

OVM—Orbiting velocity meter (manufactured by American Bosch Arma Corp., Garden City, N. Y.).

OWF—Optimum working frequency.

OWG—Oil, water, gas.

OWR—Omega West reactor (research reactor at Los Alamos, N. Mex.).

OWS—Operational weather support.   OZ—Ozone.
OX—Oxygen.

P

P—Launching from a ground-level pad (Department of Defense missile designation). Pencil tube. Pentode. Plate (anode). Plug. Poise. Polarization (dipole moment per unit volume). Police. Portable. Portable cord, reinforced. Power. Prime number. Probe (Air Force vehicle designation). Produce stored information for future use. Propulsion (Air Force mission designation). Punch. Soft pad (Air Force designation).

PA—Particular average. Post adjutant. Power of attorney. Pressure altitude. Program address. Public address. Pulse amplifier.

P/A—Pilotless aircraft.

PABX—Private automatic branch exchange (telephone term).

PAC—Packaged assembly circuit. Personal analog computer.

PACAF—Pacific Air Forces.

PACCS—Post-attack command control system.

PACE—Packaged cram executive. Precision analog computing equipment (manufactured by Electronic Associates, Long Branch, N.J.). Producers of Associated Components for Electronics (trade association).

PACE-S/C—Preflight acceptance checkout equipment for spacecraft.

PACM—Pulse amplitude code modulation.

PACOR—Passive correlation (developed by Fairchild).

PACORE—Parabolic corner reflector.

PACT—Position, attitude, and trajectory control. Production analysis control technique. Program for automatic coding techniques (compiler for IBM-701 computer). Programmed automatic circuit tester (developed by General Electric).

PADAR—Passive airborne detection and ranging.

PADT—Post-alloy diffusion transistor.

PAE—Port of aerial embarkation.

PAFB—Patrick Air Force Base.

PAG—Professional Activities Group (within the Society of Plastics Engineers).

PAI—Precise angle indicator.

PAIL—Post-attack intercontinental link.

PAL—Peripheral access lattices.

PAM—Portable alpha monitor. Pulse amplitude modulation.

PAQR—Polyacene-quinone radical (organic semiconductor).

PAR—Pennsylvania advanced reactor. Physiological aging rate. Precision approach radar (air traffic control). Production automated riveting (manufactured by Tubular Rivet and Stud Co.). Progressive aircraft rework.

PARADE—Passive-active range determination (Army's electronic counter-countermeasures system developed by Sylvania).

PARAMI—Parsons active ring-around miss indicator (developed by the Ralph M. Parsons Co.).

PARCA—Projectile autopropulse radio-guid contre avion (French missile).

PARIS—Pulse analysis-recording information system.

PARS—Pilotless Aircraft Research Station (Wallops Island, Va.).

PARSEV—Paraglider research vehicle.

PARTAC—Precision Askania range target acquisition and control.

PARTEI—Purchasing Agents of the Radio, TV and Electronics Industries.

PARTNER—Proof of analog results through a numerical equivalent routine (developed by Honeywell).

PAS—Pilot's attack sight (developed by Ferranti Ltd.). Polish Astronautical Society. Professional activity study (computer system for hospital medical recording data). Public address system.

PASCAL—Philips automatic sequence calculator (developed by N. V. Philips, Gloeilampenfabrieken, Holland).

PAT—Parametric artificial talker. Plenum air track. Position-adjusting type. Production assessment test.

PATA—Plenum air tread amphibian.

PAT-C—Position, attitude, trajectory control (developed by Marquardt Corp.).

PATN—Pattern.

PATSU—Patrol aircraft service unit.

PAUDGET—Photometer, automated universal distribution gonioelectric type.

PAV—Phase angle voltmeter.

PAWS—Programmed automatic welding system.

PAX—Private automatic exchange (telephone term).

PB—Pentaborane (rocket fuel). Peripheral buffer. Phonetically balanced (audio term). Power boiler. Push button (JIC and NMTBA term).

PBAA—Polybutadiene acrylic acid (a hydrocarbon polymer used as a solid propellant binder).

PBI—Process branch indicator.

PBP—Push button panel.

PBR—Pebble bed reactor.

PBX—Private branch exchange.

PBY—Twin-engine amphibian patrol bomber.

PC—Petty cash. Photoconductor. Picture. Plastic core. Power contactor (JIC and NMTBA term). Pressure controller. Primary center. Printed circuits. Program counter. Provisional costs. Pulse controller (telephone term). Punched card. Submarine chaser (U.S. Navy).

P-C—Polar to Cartesian.

PCA—Polar cap absorption. Pool critical assembly.

PCC—Polarity-coincidence correlator. Positive control communications.

PCDS—Power conversion and distribution system.

PCE—Submarine chaser escort (U.S. Navy).

PCEA—Pacific Coast Electrical Association.

PCEP—Predicted comparative failure probability (reliability term).

PCH—Patrol craft, hydrofoil.

PCI—Panel call indicator (telephone term). Pattern correspondence index (intelligibility measure). Peripheral command indicator (developed by Collins Radio). Prestressed Concrete Institute.

PCL—Printed circuit lamp.

PCLA—Power control linkage assembly (developed by Bendix Corp.).

PCM—Passive countermeasures. Pulse code modulation.

PCMP—Packed-computational.

PCM-PS—Pulse code modulation, phase-shift.

PCNS—Polar coordinate navigation system.

PCO—Procuring contract officer.

PCP—Preassembled cable in pipe. Program change proposal.

PCQ—Production control quantometer.

PCR—Program control register. Pulse compression radar.

PCS—Permanent change of station. Planning control sheet. Program counter store (computer term—Mobidic). Punched card system. Submarine chaser sweepers (U.S. Navy).

PCT—Paper crepe tape. Portable camera-transmitter. Potential-current transformer. Pressure-concentration temperature.

PCTFE—Polychlorotrifluoroethylene.

PCTR—Physical constants test reactor.

PD—Paid. Per diem. Plate dissipation. Positive displacement. Potential difference. Procurement division. Projected display. Proximity detector. Pulse driver. Pulse duration. Pulse-doppler. Twisted portable cord.

Pd—Pedestal.

PDA—Probability distribution analyzer.

PDC—Prevention-of-deterioration center (National Academy of Sciences—National Research Council).

PDF—Probability distribution function.

PDI—Pilot direction indicator.

PDM—Pulse duration modulation.

PDP—Process development pile. Programmed data processor. Project development plan.

PDQ—Programmed data quantizer.

PDR—Precision depth recorder.

Predetection recording. Preliminary data report. Process dynamics recorder (system for recording process data on magnetic tape for presentation to a computer).

PDRC—Pressure-difference-recording controller.

PDT—Panoramic design technique.

PE—Eagle boat (U.S. Navy). Permanent echo (radar term). Processing element. Port of embarkation. Professional engineer.

PEAC—Photoelectric autocollimator (developed by Barnes Engineering, Stamford, Conn.).

PEC—Photoelectric cell.

PEEP—Pilot's electronic eye-level presentation (developed by Rank Cintel, England).

PEG—Principle of the equivalent generator.

PEI—Porcelain Enamel Institute (Associations Bldg., 1145 19th St. N.W., Washington, D.C.). Professional Engineers in Industry (section of NSPE).

PELC—Professional Engineers' Legislative Committee.

PEM—Photoelectromagnetic.

PENNSTAC—Penn State University automatic digital computer.

PEP—Peak envelope power. Planar epitaxial passivated (transistor). Princeton experimental package (developed for Orbiting Astronomical Observatory — OAO). Program evaluation procedure (Air Force system patterned after Navy's PERT).

PEPP—Professional Engineers in Private Practice (section of NSPE).

PER—Person-to-person.

PERCOS—Performance coding system (digital system of classifying manufacturers' data on components, developed by E. A. Keller (Motorola, Inc.).

PERT—Program evaluation review technique (computerized management of Polaris research and development).

PET—Position-event-time. Process evaluation tester. Production environmental testing.

PETA—Portable electronic traffic analyzer (radar speed meter developed by Marconi Co., Essex, England).

PETP—Polyethylene terephthalate (polyester-film capacitor).

PETS—Pacific Electronic Trade Show (business office, 2216 S. Hill St., Los Angeles 7, Calif.).

PEXRAD—Programmed electronic X-ray automatic diffractometer (developed by Bell Labs, Murray Hill, N.J.).

PF—Frigate (U.S. Navy). Perchloryl fluoride (rocket liquid propellant oxidizer). Power factor.

pf—Picofarad.

PFA—Pure fluid amplification.

PFAM—Programmed frequency-amplitude modulator.

PFC—Motor boat submarine chaser (U. S. Navy).

PFEFES—Pacific and Far East Federation of Engineering Societies.

PFG—Primary frequency generator.

PFM—Pressure flow meter. Pulse frequency modulation.

PFNS—Position-fixing and navigation system (developed by Bendix-Pacific under Signal Corps contract).

PFR—Polarized field frequency relay. Preliminary flight rating.

PFRT—Preliminary flight rating test.

PFT—Paper, flat tape.

PFV—Repetitive peak forward blocking voltage.

PG—Gunboat or corvette (U.S. Navy).

PGA—Professional Group — Audio (IRE).

PGAC—Professional Group—Automatic Control (IRE).

PGANE—Professional Group—Aeronautical and Navigational Electronics (IRE).

PGAP—Professional Group—Antennas and Propagation (IRE).

PGBTR—Professional Group—Broadcast and TV Receivers (IRE).

PGBTS—Professional Group—Broadcast Transmission Systems (IRE).

PGCP—Professional Group — Component Parts (IRE).

PGCS—Professional Group — Communications Systems (IRE).

PGCT—Professional Group—Circuit Theory (IRE).

PGE—Professional Group — Education (IRE).

PGEC—Professional Group — Electronic Computers (IRE).

PGED—Professional Group — Electronic Devices (IRE).

PGEM—Professional Group — Engineering Management (IRE).

PGEWS—Professional Group — Engineering Writing and Speech (IRE).

PGHFE—Professional Group — Human Factors in Electronics (IRE).

PGI—Professional Group — Instrumentation (IRE).

PGIE—Professional Group — Industrial Electronics (IRE).

PGIT—Professional Group — Information Theory (IRE).

PGME—Professional Group—Medical Electronics (IRE).

PGMTT—Professional Group—Microwave Theory and Techniques (IRE).

PGNS—Professional Group — Nuclear Science (IRE).

PGPEP—Professional Group — Product Engineering and Production (IRE).

PGPT—Professional Group — Production Techniques (IRE).

PGR—Precision graphic recorder.

PGRFI—Professional Group — Radio-Frequency Interference (IRE).

PGRQC—Professional Group — Reliability and Quality Control (IRE).

PGTRC—Professional Group — Space Electronics and Telemetry (IRE).

PGUE—Professional Group—Ultrasonic Engineering (IRE).

PGVC—Professional Group — Vehicular Communications (IRE).

PH—Performance history (reliability term). Phone (headphone). Photographer's mate (U. S. Navy).

Ph—Phase.

PHA—Pulse-height analyzer (British).

PHD—Pulse-height discrimination.

PHI—Position and homing indicator.

pHI—pH indicator.

PHONO—Phonograph.

PHP—Planetary horizon platform.

PHR—Parts per hundred of rubber.

pHR—pH recorder.

pHRC—pH recording controller.

PHS—Public Health Service.

PHT—Phototube.

PI—Performance index. Plaster. Pressure indicator. Printer (U. S. Navy). Programmed instruction.

PIANC—Permanent International Association of Navigation Congresses (American section PIANC —c/o Board of Engineers for Rivers and Harbors, Washington 25, D.C.).

PIC—Procurement Information Center. (U. S. Air Force). Program interrupt control.

PICE—Programmable integrated control equipment (developed by Systems Div., Beckman Instruments, Inc., Anaheim, Calif., for Lockheed—1960).

PIE—Plug-in electronics.

PIG—Pendulous integrating gyro.

PIGA—Pendulous integrating gyro accelerometer.

PIGMI—Position-indicating general measuring instrument.

PILAC—Pulsed ion linear accelerator (developed by Los Alamos Scientific Laboratory).

PILC—Paper - insulated, lead - covered cable.

PILOT—Pilot data processor (developed by National Bureau of Standards).

PILP—Pseudo - infinite, logarithmically periodic (antenna).

PIM—Precision indicator of the meridian (developed by English Electric Aviation Ltd., England). Precision instrument mount (developed by AMF).

PIN—Positive-intrinsic-negative.

PINO—Positive input—negative output.

PIO—Precision iterative operation. Public information officer.

PIP—Persistent internal polarization (computer memory term).

PIPER—Pulsed intense plasma for exploratory research.

PIQSY—Probe for International Quiet Solar Year.

PIR—Parachute infantry regiment. Personnel information report.

PIRAD—Proximity information, range and disposition.

PIRT—Precision infrared tracking (laser tracking system developed by Perkin-Elmer Corp. and Spectra-Physics, Inc.).

PIV—Peak inverse voltage. Positive, infinitely variable (speed control manufactured by Link-Belt).

PJ—Vinyl plastic jacket.

PL—Plate. Plateau length. Plug (JIC and NMTBA term).

PLAN—Positive locator aid to navigation (developed by General Precision, Inc.).

PLASTEC—Plastics evaluation center (Dept. of Defense, Picatinny Arsenal, Dover, N. J.).

PLAT—Pilot/LSO landing-aid television (developed by RCA to tape-record pilot landings on aircraft carriers).

PLATO—Programmed logic for automatic teaching operations (developed by the Coordinated Science Laboratory, University of Illinois).

PLC—Power - line communications. Private line carrier (telephone term).

PLC-DR—Private line carrier-divided ringing (telephone term).

PLD—Principle of limit design.

PLdF—Pseudo load factor.

PLENCH—Pliers-wrench (nut-and-bolt tool developed by Ling-Temco-Vought).

PLF—Private-line telephone. Positive lock fastener. Proposition-letter formula.

PLI—Pilot-location indicator.

PLN—Plan.

PLO—Phase-locked oscillator.

PLPS—Propellant loading and pressurization system.

PLS—Pulser.

PLT—Planar tube. Private line teletype. Private line teletypewriter. Pulsed-light theodolite (developed by Motorola).

PLUTO—Programmed logic for automatic teaching (developed by University of Illinois).

PM—Permanent magnet. Photomultiplier. Post meridian. Production manager. Prone mounting. Provost marshal. Pulse modulator.

PMA—Phonograph Manufacturers' Association. Plastic mockup assembly. Pole-mounted amplifier. Poor man's Azusa. Precision Measurements Association. Pyromellitic acid (used in epoxy production).

PMC—Powdered metal cathode.

PMDA—Pyromellitic dianhydride (used in epoxy production; developed by DuPont).

PME—Photomagnetoelectric. Precision measuring equipment.

PMEA—Powder Metallurgy Equipment Association.

PMEMA—Powder Metallurgy Equipment Manufacturers' Association.

PMEV—Panel-mounting electronic voltmeter.

PMG—Permanent magnet generator.

PMI—Pressed Metal Institute (3673 Lee Rd., Cleveland 20, Ohio). Purchased-materials inspection.

PMMA—Polymethyl methacrylate.

PMMC—Permanent - magnet movable-coil.

PMPMA—Powder Metallurgy Parts Manufacturers' Association.

PMR—Pacific misslie range.

PMRSG—Pacific Missile Range Study Group.

PMS—Permanent - magnet speaker. Plastic-to-metal seal.

PMST—Professor of Military Science and Tactics.

PMT — Permanent magnet tester. Pulse modulator tube.

PMU—Portable memory unit.

PMW—Private microwave system.

PN—Perceived noise level. Phon.

PND—Present next digit.

PNM—Pulse number modulation.

PNT—Propulsion wind tunnel.

PO—Rayon parallel lamp cord. Petty officer (U. S. Navy). Power output. Primary outlet (telephone term). Project office.

POC—Planning objective coordinators. Productional operational capability.

POGO—Polar Orbiting Geophysical Observatory.

POL—Problem-oriented language.

POLY—Polyethylene.

POM—Preparation for overseas movement.

POMS—Panel on Operational Meteorogical Satellites.

POMSEE—Performance, operational and maintenance standards for electronic equipment (U.S. Navy).

POP—Pneumatically operated piston.

POPD—Plans, Operations and Programs Division (Signal Corps).

POR—Payable on receipt. Preparation for overseas movement of individuals (U. S. Army).

PORT—Photo-optical recorder tracker.

POSIP—Portable ship instrumentation package.

POSJ—Rubber, parallel lamp cord.

POSS—Passive optical satellite surveillance (developed by RCA for U. S. Air Force Electronic Systems Division). Prototype optical surveillance system.

POT—Plastic parallel lamp cord.

POTS—Photo-optical terrain simulator (manufactured by Fairchild Camera and Instrument Corp).

PP—Pilot punch.

PPA—Preliminary pile assembly (reactor, Knolls Atomic Power Lab, Schenectady, N. Y.). Preliminary power laboratory.

PPB—Provisioning parts breakdown.

PPC—Potential performance capability.

PPCS—Person - to - person, collect, credit card, or third-party charge (telephone term).

PPD—Pellon polishing disc (used in polishing semiconductor materials). Plans and Programs Division (Signal Corps).

PPDD—Plan position data display.

PPM—Periodic permanent magnets (used for forcusing traveling-wave tubes). Pulse position modulation.

ppm—Parts per million.

PPMA—Precision Potentiometer Manufacturers' Association.

PPN—Production progress notifications.

PPO—Prior permission only.

PPS—Programming program Strela (automatic program for "Strela" —Russian computer).

pps—Pulses per second.

PPSN—Present position.

PPTP—Power proportioning temperature programmer.

PPV—Pitch power valves.

PQ—Premium quality.

PQAA—Province of Quebec Association of Architects (Canadian organization).

PQC—Picture quality control.

PR—Parachute rigger (U. S. Navy). Periodic reversal. Position register. Pressure recorder. Principal register. Print. Printer module. Program register. River gunboat (U. S. Navy).

Pr—Permanent polarization.

PRA—Pitch and roll attitude. Print alphanumerically.

PRC—Pressure-recording controller.

PRD—Print hexadecimally.

PRDV—Peak - reading digital voltmeter.

PREP—Programmed educational package (educational computer system developed by Remington Rand).

PRES—Pressure.

PRESS—Pacific range electromagnetic signature study (a product of the Advanced Research Projects Agency).

PRESSDUCTOR—Pressure inductor.

PRESTO—Project release status operation (developed by Convair Div., General Dynamics).

PRF—Pulse-repetition frequency.

PRI—Pressure-ratio indicator. Primary. Pulse-rate indicator.

PRIME—Programmed instruction for management education.

PRIMSCO—Pilot run item master schedule committee (planning system developed by Aerojet-General Corp.).

PRIOR—Program for in-orbit rendezvous (Boeing study of antisatellite weapon).

PRIP—Parts reliability improvement program (developed by AC Spark Plug Div., General Motors Corp.).

PRISE—Program for integrated shipboard electronics (U. S. Navy Bureau of Ships).

PRISM—Program reliability information system for management.

PRL—Periodic requirements.

PRM—Personal radiation monitor.

PRO—Print octal.

PROCTOR—Priority routing organizer for computer transfers and operations of registers (developed by Ferranti).

PRODAC—Programmed digital automatic control.

PROFAC—Propulsive fluid accumulator.

PROLAN—Processed language (simplified computer language developed by Socony Mobile Oil Co.).

PROOF—Precision recording optical of fingerprints (developed by Chance Vought Aircraft).

PROP—Planetary rocket ocean platform (sea-based launcher designed by Aerojet-General Corp.).

PRP—Pseudo-random pulse.

PRR—Pawling research reactor (Pawling, N. Y.). Pulse repetition rate.

PRS—Pattern recognition system.

PRT—Printer. Program reference table (Burroughs computer term).

PRTOT—Prototype real-time optical tracker (designed by Measurement Systems, Inc.).

PRTR—Plutonium recycle test reactor (Richland, Wash.).

PRV—Peak reverse voltage.

PRW—Per cent rated wattage.

PS—Extruded polyethylene dielectric. Parity switch. Planning and scheduling. Plateau slope. Polarity selector. Power supply. Pressure switch (JIC and NMTBA term). Public safety. Pulse shaper.

P-S—Pressure-sensitive.

P/S—Point of shipment.

Ps—Spontaneous polarization.

PSA—Pressure-sensitive adhesive.

PSAC—President's Scientific Advisory Committee.

PSAD—Prediction, simulation, adaptation and decision.

PSCRT—Passive satellite communications research terminal.

PSCS—Pacific scatter communication system (6500-mile communication system from Oahu, Hawaii, to Luzon, Philippines).

PSD—Phase-sensitive detector. Pulse shape discrimination.

PSE—Please. Pressurized subcritical experiment.

PSF—Power separation filter.

PSG—Pulsed strain gage.

PSH—Three-conductor cable, extra-heavy insulation.

psig—Pounds per square inch, gage.

PSK—Phase-shift-keyed.

PSM—Pre-synaptic membrane.

PSMR—Parts specification management for reliability.

PSMT—Pedestal sight manipulation test.

PSNR—Power signal-to-noise ratio.

PSO—Pad safety officer.

PSS—Personal signalling system (telephone term).

PSSC—Physical Science Study Committee (organized in 1956 at Massachusetts Institute of **[Cont.]**

Technology).

PST—Pressure-sensitive tape.

PSVM—Phase-sensitive voltmeter.

PSW—Potentiometer slidewire. Pro-submarine warfare.

PSWR—Power standing-wave ratio.

PT—Motor torpedo boat (U. S. Navy). Paper tape. Pencil tube. Point location. Positional toler-ancing. Potential transformer. Pulse train.

PTA—Phototransistor amplifier. Pitch trim adjustment.

PTBR—Punched tape block reader.

PTC—Motor boat submarine chaser (U. S. Navy). Pitch trim compen-sator. Power transfer coefficient. Pulse time code.

PTCV—Pilot-operated temperature-control valve.

PTDTL—Pumped tunnel diode-transistor logic.

PTFE—Polytetrafluoroethelyene.

PTGC—Programmed temperature gas chromatography.

PTL—Pressure, torque, or load.

PTM—Pulse time modulation.

PTO—Port transportation officer. Power takeoff.

PTP—Point-to-point.

PTR—Pool test reactor. Pressure tube reactor. Pre-transmit receiv-ing.

PTS—Photogrammetric triangula-tion system. **Points.**

PTT—Push-to-talk.

PTVAA—Portland TV Appliance Association (424 Failing Bldg., Portland, Ore.).

PTX—Polythermalex (magnet wire).

PU—Pickup. Propellant utilization.

PUP—Peripheral unit processor (computer term).

PUSE—Propellant utilization system exerciser.

PV—Photovoltaic. **Primary valve.** Public voucher.

PVC—Polyvinyl chloride. Potential volume change.

PVD—Paravisual director (devel-oped by Smiths Aviation Division, England).

PVF—Polyvinyl fluoride.

PVM—Projection video monitor.

PW—Pulse width. Moistureproof re-inforced cord.

PWAFRR—Present worth of all future revenue requirements.

PWB—Printed wiring board.

PWC—Pulse-width coded.

PWD—Pulse-width discriminator.

PWE—Pulse-width encoder.

PWI—Pilot warning indicator. Pilot warning instrument. Proximity warning indicator.

PWM—Pulse-width modulation.

PWP—Moistureproof, reinforced portable cord.

PWR—Pressurized water reactor.

PWS—Predicted wave signalling. Private wire system.

PX—Pressure transmitter.

PXA—Pulsed xenon arc (a quartz lamp manufactured by General Electric).

PXM—Propection X-ray microscope.

PY—Converted yacht (U. S. Navy).

PZT — Lead zirconate-titanate (a common synthetic piezoelectric material).

Q

Q—Drone (Department of Defense missile designation). Target (Air Force mission designation). Un-derwater sound equipment.

QA—Quality assurance.

QAVC—Quiet automatic volume

control.

QCW—Quadrature-phase subcarrier signal.

QCWA—Quarter Century Wireless Association.

QDC—Quick dependable communications.

QDM—Quick disconnector, miniature.

QDRI—Qualitative development requirements information (U. S. Army Ordnance program).

QF—Quality factor.

QFM—Quantized frequency modulation.

QG—Quadrature grid.

QIT—Quality information and test system (developed by General Electric Co., Waynesboro, Va.).

QM—Quadrature modulation. Quartermaster (U. S. Navy).

QMC—Quartermaster Corps.

QMFCI—Quartermaster Food and Container Institute (1819 W. Pershing Rd., Chicago, Ill.).

QMGEC—Chief of Organization Planning and Control Division, Quartermaster Corps.

QMGRE—Director of Military Planning Division of Quartermaster Corps.

QMI—Qualification maintainability inspection.

QMQB—Quick-make, quick-break.

QMR&EC—Quartermaster Research and Engineering Command (Natick, Mass.).

QMS—Quartermaster sergeant.

QMSO—Quartermaster Supply Officer.

QNH—Altimeter setting above mean sea level.

QNT—Quantizer.

QOR—Qualitative operational requirement.

QP—Quasi-peak.

QPB—Quantized probability design.

QPL—Qualified producers list. Qualified products list.

QQPRI—Qualitative and quantitative planning requirements information.

QR—Quick reaction.

QRA—Quality reliability assurance.

QRC—Quick reaction capability (Air Force program).

QSSP—Quasi-solid-state panel (display panel manufactured by Maico Electronics, Minneapolis).

QUAD—Quadrant.

QUAP—Questionnaire analysis program.

R

R—Code rubber-covered wire. Degrees Rankine. Radio. Radiolocation. Railroad car (Air Force designation). Read. Reading. Receiving. Reconnaissance (Air Force mission designation). Regulator. Repeater (telephone term). Reset. Resistance. Resistor. Reverse (JIC and NMTBA term). Right. Rocket (Dept. of Defense missile designation). 600-volt copper conductor used for power wiring.

r—Roentgen (unit: amount of radiation).

RA—Rear admiral. Receiver attenuation. Receiver auxiliary relay. Register allotter. Right ascension. Rosin acid.

Ra—Rational number.

RAAF—Royal Australian Air Force.

RAB—Rotating arm basin (David Taylor model basin).

RABAL—Radiosonde balloon wind data.

RAC—Read address counter. Research Advisory Committee.

RACE—Rapid automatic checkout equipment (designed by Sperry; new version under development by Airborne Instruments Lab.).

RACEP—Random access and correlation for extended performance (communications system developed by The Martin Co.).

RACES—Radio Amateur Civil Emergency Service (amateur civil defense organization).

RACON—Radar beacon.

RAD—Radiac. Radiation dose unit (energy absorption of 100 ergs per gram).

RADAN—Radar doppler autonavigator (developed by General Precision Laboratories).

RADAR—Radio detection and ranging.

RADARC—Radially distributed annular rocket combustion chamber.

RADAS—Random access discrete address system (developed by Motorola, Inc.).

RADAT—Radar data transmission system. Radio direction and track. Radiosonde observation data.

RADATAC—Radiation data acquisition chart (developed by Radiation, Inc.).

RADC—Rome Air Development Center.

RadCM—Radar countermeasures.

RADFAC—Radiating facility for aircraft flight line testing (developed by Republic Aviation for preflight inspection of electronic gear in the F-105).

RAD HAZ—Radio - frequency hazard. Radiation hazard.

RADIC—Redifon analog - digital computing system (developed by Redifon Ltd., Sussex, England).

RADIST—Radar Distance indicator.

RADOP—Radar/optical (tow target

system developed by Del Mar Engineering Labs).

RADSKY—Radar screens.

RAE—Royal Aircraft Establishment (British counterpart of the FAA).

RAeS—Royal Aeronautical Society.

RAF—Royal Air Force.

RAFAR—Radio automated facsimile and reproduction.

RAFD—Rome Air Force Depot.

RAFT — Recomp algebraic formula translator (used with Autonetics' recomp computer).

RAI—Italian Broadcasting System.

RAM—Radio attenuation measurement.

RAMA—Rome Air Materiel Area.

RAMAC—Random-access method of accounting control (IBM computer).

RAMARK—Radar marker.

RAMP—Raytheon airborne microwave platform.

RAMPART—Radar advanced measurements program for analysis of re-entry techniques (U. S. Air Force radar system developed by Raytheon Co.).

RAMPS—Resource allocation and multi-project scheduling.

RAMS—Radio Amateur Megacycle Society. Right ascension mean sun.

RAN—Read-around-number.

RANDAM—Random-access nondestructive advanced memory.

RANDID—Rapid alphanumeric digital indicating device (manufactured by Hazeltine Corp.).

RANDO—Radiotherapy analog dosimetry.

RAO—Radio - astronomical observatory.

RAOB—Radiosonde observation.

RAPC—Radio Administrative Plenipotentiary Conference (drafts ITU Convention).

RAPCOE—Random-access programming and checkout equipment

(manufactured by Minneapolis-Honeywell).

RAPCON—Radar approach control facility (U. S. Air Force).

RAPID—Relative address programming implementation device. Rocketdyne automatic processing of integrated data. Ryan automatic plot indicator device (developed by Ryan Aeronautical Co.).

RAR—Radio acoustic ranging. Regular Army Reserve. Remove audible ring.

RARAD—Radar advisory.

RAREP—Radar weather report.

RARET—Radio Free Europe.

RAS—Royal Aeronautical Society.

RASER—Radio-frequency amplification by stimulated emission of radiation. Range- and sensitivity-extending resonator.

RASES—Republic Aviation Society of Engineers and Scientists (Farmingdale, L. I., N. Y.).

RASTAC—Random - access storage and control (manufactured by Laboratory for Electronics, Inc., 1079 Commonwealth Ave., Boston, Mass.).

RASTAD—Random - access storage and display (developed by LFE, Inc.).

RAT—Ram air temperature. Rocket-assisted torpedo.

RATAN—Radar and television aid to navigation.

RATCC—Radar Air Traffic Control Center (U. S. Navy).

RATE—Remote automatic telemetry equipment (developed by Shand & Jurs Co.).

RATO—Rocket-assisted takeoff.

RATT—Radio teletype.

RAVU—Radiosonde analysis and verification unit.

RAYCI—Raytheon controlled inventory.

RB—Read backward. Read buffer.

Return-to-bias. Reserse blocked. Ring back.

RBC—Remote balance control (stereo control developed by Victor Co. of Japan).

RBDE—Radar bright display equipment.

RBE—Radiation biological effectiveness. Relative biological effectiveness.

RBS—Radar bomb-scoring. Recoverable booster system.

RC—Ray-control electrode. Read and compute. Reader code. Reference cavity. Regional center (telephone term). Reserve Corps. Resolver control. Rosin core.

RCAF—Royal Canadian Air Force.

RCAG—Remote control air to ground.

RCC—Read (write) channel continue. Reader common contact. Remote communications complex.

RCE—Rapid circuit etch.

RCEEA — Radio Communications and Electronic Engineering Association.

RCF—Recall finder.

RCG — Reverberation-controlled gain.

RCI—Read (write) channel initialize.

RCM—Radar countermeasures.

RCN — Netherlands Reactor Centrum. Royal Canadian Navy.

RCO — Remote-control oscillator. Rendezvous-compatible orbit. Representative calculating operation. Research Contracting Officer.

RCOA—Radio Club of America.

RCPA—Rural Cooperative Power Association.

RCR—Reader control relay.

RCS—Rearward communications system.

RCSC—Radio Component Standardization Committee (British agency of The Ministry of Supply

121

—grants component type approvals).

RC-SCE—Relative composite rating.

RCT—Resolver control transformer.

RCTL—Resistor - capacitor coupled transistor logic.

RCV—Relative conductor volume.

RD—Radar display. Radarman (U. U. Navy). Recognition differential. Redefines. Relay driver.

R & D—Research and development.

RDA—Research and Development Abstracts (published by Division of Technical Information, U. S. Atomic Energy Commission).

RDB—Research and Development Board. Round die bushing.

RDBL—Readable.

RDE—Research and Development Establishment (British).

RDF—Radio direction finder. Reflection direction finding.

RDG—Resolver differential generator.

RDL—Replaceable lamp display light.

RDME—Range- and distance-measuring equipment.

RDO—Radio. Read out.

RDP—Radar data processing.

RDR—Radar.

RDT—Remote data transmitter. Rotational direction transmission (sonar term).

RDT & E—Research, development, test, and evaluation.

RE—Royal Engineers.

Re—Real number. Reset

Re+—Positive real number.

REA—Rural Electrification Administration.

REAC—Reeves electronic analog computer.

REACT—Radio Emergency Association Citizens Teams (volunteer CB radio operators). Rese Engineering automatic core tester.

READ — Radar echo augmentation device (used in drones to make them appear as large as a bomber on radar presentations).

REASTAN—Renton electrical analog for solution of thermal analogous networks (developed by Boeing Co., Renton, Wash.).

REB—Re-entry body building. Roentgen equivalent biological.

REBATRON—Relativistic electron buncher and accelerator (developed at the University of Illinois).

REC—Receiver. Rectifier (JIC and NMTBA term).

RECG—Radioelectrocardiograph.

RECIPE—Recomp computer interpretive program expeditor.

RECMF—Radio and Electronic Component Manufacturers' Federation (Great Britain).

RECP—Receptacle (JIC and NMTBA term).

RED—Reducing.

REEG — Radioelectroencephalograph.

REG—Rheoencephalograph (differential cerebral blood-flow sensor).

REGAL—Range and elevation guide for approach and landing (developed by Gilfillan Bros.).

REIC—Radiation Effects Information Center (Battelle Memorial Institute).

REINS—Radar - equipped inertial navigation system (manufactured by Autonetics).

REL—Rate of energy loss.

REM—Rapid eye movement.

rem—Roentgen equivalent man (radiation term: amount of radiation which produces the same biological effect as one roentgen of X or gamma radiation.

REMAB—Radiation-equivalent manikin absorption.

REMAD—Remote magnetic anomaly detector.

REMC—Resin - encapsulated mica

capacitor (developed by Cornell-Dubilier.).

REMCAL — Radiation - equivalent manikin calibration.

REMG—Radioelectromyograph.

REML—Radiation effects mobile lab (employed by U. S. Signal Corps).

REO — Regenerated electrical output.

rep—Roentgen equivalent physical (radiation unit: Any radiation which deposits 93 ergs in 1 gram of animal tissue).

REPERF—Reperforator.

REPM—Representatives of Electronic Products Manufacturers.

REP-OP—Repetitive Operation.

REPPAC—Repetitively pulsed plasma accelerator (developed by General Electric Co.).

RER—Radiation effects reactor (Air Force facility at Georgia Nuclear Laboratories, Dawsonville, Ga.—operated by Lockheed Nuclear Products).

RERL—Residual equivalent return loss.

RES—Resistor (JIC and NMTBA term). Reticulo-endothelial system.

RESA—Scientific Research Society of America.

RESCU—Rocket ejection seat catapult, upward.

RESILRIG—Resilience and rigidity.

RET—Return (JIC term).

RETIMP—Raleigh-Edwards tensile impact machine pendulum.

REVOCON—Remote volume control (developed by Altec Lansing Corp.).

REVOP—Random evolutionary operation.

REW—Rewind.

RF—Radio frequency. Range finder. Rapid fire. Read forward. Reception fair. Register finder. Resistance factor. Reverse free. Rubber-covered fixture wire, solid or 7-

strand. Running forward (computer term—tape).

RFA—Radio - frequency authorization.

RFC—Radio-frequency choke. Royal Flying Corps.

RFCO—Range Facilities Control Officer.

RFCP—Radio Frequency Compatibility Program (established in June 1960 by U. S. Dept. of Defense).

RFD—Reactor flight demonstration. Re-entry flight demonstration.

RFE—Radio Free Europe.

RFFD—Radio-frequency fault detection.

RFH—Heat-resistant, rubber-covered fixture wire, solid or 7-strand.

RFI—Radio-frequency interference. Requests for information.

RFNA—Red fuming nitric acid (missile fuel oxidizer).

RFP—Request for proposal.

RFQ—Request for quote.

RFR—Reject failure rate.

RFS—Regardless of feature size. Rover Flight Safety Office (Project Rover).

RFW—Reversible full-wave.

RFWAC—Reversible full-wave alternating current.

RFWDC—Reversible full-wave direct current.

RG—Range. Rate-grown. Reception good. Register. Reset gate. Reverse gate.

RGB—Red-green-blue (color TV term).

RGE—Range.

RG(N)—Register (N stages).

RH—Heat - resistant rubber - covered wire. Relative humidity. Rheostat (JIC and NMTBA term). Right-handed.

RHH—Heat-resistant rubber wire (high-temperature).

RHI—Range-height indicator.

RHP—Radiant heat pump.

RHRW—Tinned copper conductors, rubber-insulated, saturated braid, flame- and moisture-resistant wire for moist locations.

RHW—Moisture- and heat-resistant rubber-covered wire (high-temperature). Reversible half-wave.

RHWAC—Reversible half-wave alternating current.

RHWACDC—Reversible half-wave alternating current-direct current.

RHWDC—Reversible half-wave direct current.

RI—Radio - influence. Radio interference. Reliability index. Reverberation index.

RIAA—Recording Industry Association of America.

RIAS—Research Institute for Advanced Studies (division of the Martin Co.).

RIC—Radio Industry Council (British organization).

RID—Radio Intelligence Division (FCC).

RIE—Royal Institute of Engineers (Netherlands organization).

RIF—Reliability improvement factor.

RIFI—Radio-interference field intensity.

RIFT—Reactor-in-flight-test.

RIL—Radio-influence level. Radio-interference level.

RIM—Receipt, inspection, maintenance.

RIND—Research Institute of National Defence (Swedish agency).

RIOT—Resolution of initial operational techniques.

RIPS—Range Instrumentation Planning Study.

RIQAP—Reduced Inspection Quality Assurance Program.

RISE—Research in supersonic environment.

RITA—Recoverable interplanetary transport approach.

RIV—Radio-influence voltage.

RKG—Radioelectrocardiograph.

RL—Relay logic. Return loss. 600-volt tin-copper conductors used in moist locations.

RLBG—Relative bearing.

RLC—Remote line concentrator. Run length coding.

RLJFJ — Rubber-lead-jute-flat armor-jute, metallic parkway cables for underground use.

RLM—Rearward-launched missile.

RLTS—Radio-linked telemetry system.

RM—Radioman (U. S. Navy). Reaction mass. Readout matrix.

RMI — Radio magnetic indicator. Reliability maturity index.

RMS—Root-mean-square.

RMSE—Root-mean-square error.

RN—Radionavigation. Reception nil. Royal Navy (British).

RNA—Ribonucleic acid.

RNCF—Royal Netherlands Chemical Foundation.

RNG—Radio range.

RNM—Radionavigation mobile.

RNV—Radio-noise voltage.

RO — Range operation. Receiving only. Regimental order.

ROAD—Reorganization of the Army Divisions.

ROAMA—Rome Air Materiel Area.

ROAR—RPC-4000 Optimizing Assembly Routine (for the General Precision RPC-4000 computer).

ROBIN—Rocket balloon instrument.

ROBO—Rocket orbital bomber project (U. S. Air Force).

ROC—Required Operational Capabiltiy. Reserve Officer Candidate.

ROCAT—Rocket catapult.

RODIAC—Rotary dual input for analog computation (developed by Trio Labs).

ROI—Return on investment.

RO MON—Receiving only monitor.

ROMOTAR—Range-only measurement-of-trajectory automatic recording.

ROOT—Relaxation oscillator optically tuned (Westinghouse development).

ROOST—Reusable one-stage orbital space truck (space booster recovery scheme proposed by Douglas Aircraft).

ROPA—Reserve Officer Personnel Act.

ROPRA—Reserve Officer Performance Recording Activity (U. S. Navy).

ROR—Rocket on rotor (helicopter power system developed by Reaction Motors, Inc.).

ROSE—Rising observational sounding equipment.

ROT—Rate of turn.

ROTAC—Rotary oscillating torque actuators.

ROTEL — Rotational telemeter (manufactured by Industrial Electronics Corp., Melbourne, Fla.).

ROTI—Recording optical tracking instrument (used for satellite and missile tracking; developed by Perkin-Elmer).

ROTR—Receiving only typing reperforator.

ROTR S/P—Receiving only typing reperforator—series to parallel.

ROVD—Relay-operated voltage divider.

RP—Reception poor. Recommended practice. Remote pickup broadcast. Repeater (telephone term). Revertive pulsing. Round punch.

RPA—Radar performance analyzer.

RPC—Remote position control.

RPD—Radar prediction device. Resistance pressure detector.

RPFC—Recurrent peak forward current.

RPG—Radiation protection guide.

RPIE — Real property installed equipment.

RPL—Running program language.

RPM—Radar performance monitor. Regulated power modules.

RPMI—Revolutions-per-minute indicator.

RPMP—Register of Plan Mobilization Producers.

RPO—Rotor power output.

RPPI—Remote plan position indicator.

RPRT—Report.

RPS—Registered Publication System (Naval Security Station, Washington, D. C.). Regulated power supply.

RPSM—Resources planning and scheduling method.

RPT—Repeat.

RPVT—Relative position - velocity technique.

RR—Repetition rate or recurrence rate. Rubber-covered nonmetallic-insulated underground cable. Running reverse (computer term—tape).

RRDR—Raw radar data recorder.

RRE—Royal radar establishment (Malvern, England).

RRIC—Radar-Radio Industries of Chicago, Inc.

RRR—Range and range-rate system.

RRS—Radiation Research Society. Radio Research Station (part of the Dept. of Scientific and Industrial Research—England).

RS—Range selector. Remote station. Reset steering. Resonator. Return to saturation. Reverberation strength. Revised statutes. Rochelle salt (sodium-potassium tartrate tetrahydrate, a ferroelectric of the tartrate group). Route selector. Rubber dielectric and/or rubber sheath. Rubber seats.

RSA—Remote station alarm. Rotary switch art.

RSAF—Royal Swedish Air Force.

RSC—Range Safety Center. Relative system capability. Replacement and School Command (U. S. Army).

RSCS—Rate stabilization and control system.

RS & I—Rules, Standards, and Instructions.

RSO—Range Safety Officer.

RSP—Responder beacon.

RSS—Range safety system. Reference sound source. Relative system sensitivity. Root-sum-square.

RST—Readability, strength, tone (amateur - radio term). Resin skived tape.

RSU—Relay storage unit (teletype term).

RSVP—Radiation spectral - visual photometer.

RSW—Retarded-surface-wave.

RT—Ratio transformer. Reaction time. Receiving tube. Record transfer. Registered - transmitter (telephone term). Reset trigger. Resistor tolerance. Resistor-transistor. Room temperature.

R/T—Reperforator-transmitter unit. Rho/theta (system of air traffic control).

R & T—Research and technology.

RTA—Reliability test assembly (a digital computer developed by IBM). Rise-time analyzer.

RTASCV—Radio-TV Association of Santa Clara Valley.

RTB—Rocket test base.

RTC—Reader tape contact. Replacement Training Center (U. S. Army).

RTCA—Radio Technical Commission for Aeronautics (16th and Constitution Ave. N.W., Washington 25, D. C.).

RTCMS—Radio Technical Comission for Marine Services.

RTD—Range time decoder (devel-

oped by Astrometrics, Inc.). Resistance temperature detector.

RTDA—Radio and Television Dealers' Association (1351 Willamette Ave., Eugene, Ore.).

RTDG—Radio and TV Directors' Guild (114 E. 52nd St., New York 22, N. Y.).

RTES—Radio-TV Executives' Society, Inc.

RTF—Radiotelephone. Rocket test facility.

RTFV—Radar target folder viewer.

RTG—Radioisotope thermoelectric generator. Radiotelegraph.

RTL—Resistor-transistor logic.

RTN—Return-to-neuter.

RTP—Remote transfer point.

RTS—Radar target simulator.

RTT—Radiation tracking transducer (developed by Electro-Optical Systems, Inc.). Radioteletypewriter.

RTTAC—Radio-Television Technicians' Association of California, Inc.).

RTTY—Radioteletype.

RTV—Re-entry test vehicle. Room-temperature vulcanizing (silicone rubber insulation manufactured by General Electric).

RU—Latex - rubber - covered wire. Rockets Unlimited (1015 Atkin Ave., Salt Lake City 6, Utah).

RUB—Rubber.

RUH—Heat-resistant latex-rubber-covered wires.

RUM—Remote-controlled underseas manipulator.

RUSDIC—Russian dictionary (developed by University of California for machine language translation).

RUW—Moisture-resistant latex-rubber-covered wires.

RV—Rated voltage.

R/V—Research vessel.

RVDT—Rotary variable differential

transformer.

RVR—Runway visual range.

RW—Moisture-resistant rubber-covered wire. Read and write. Rewind.

R/W—Rights-of-way.

RWC—Read, write, and compute. Read (write) continue.

RWD—Regular world days (IGY term).

RWG—Radio Writers' Guild (6 E. 23rd St., New York, N. Y.).

RWI—Read (write)initialize. Regular world interval.

RWMA—Resistance Welding Manufacturers' Association.

RX—Resolver control transmitter.

RY—Relay.

RZ—Return-to-zero.

S

S—Elastance (measured in darafs). Salinity. Satellite (Air Force designation). Secret. Senior service, 600-volt portable cord. Sense and measure. Set. Shell. Sign. Sink. Small. Solid. Space (Air Force designation). Spool. Starting contactor (NMTBA term). Stationary. Steel. Straight side (pilot bulb designation). Strategic (Air Force mission designation). Submarine. Surface craft. Switch. Sync.

SA—Salt-acid. Select address. Service assistant. Sinuauricular. South America. Special agent.

S/A—Safe/armed.

SAAMA—San Antonio Air Materiel Area.

SAAVS — Submarine acceleration and velocity.

SAB—Scientific Advisory Board (U. S. Air Force). Signal Aviation Branch (Signal Corps).

SABRE — Secure airborne radar equipment.

SABU—SAGE backup.

SAC—Science Advisory Committee (International atomic energy agency). Special agent in charge. Store and clear accumulator. Strategic Air Command.

SACCS—Strategic Air Command control system.

SACEUR — Supreme Allied Commander of European Forces.

SACLANT—Supreme Allied Commander Atlantic.

SACO—Select address and contact operate.

SADAP—Simplified automatic data plotter.

SADSAC—Sampled - data simulator and computer.

SADT—Surface alloy diffused-base transistor.

SADTC—SHAPE Air Defense Technical Center (The Hague, Netherlands).

SAE—Shift accumulator left, excluding sign. Society of Automotive Engineers.

SAF—Secretary of the Air Force. Super abrasion furnace.

SAFB—Scott Air Force Base.

SAFI—Semiautomatic flight inspection (devised for FAA by Airborne Instruments Laboratory).

SAGE—Semiautomatic ground environment.

SAGW—Surface-to-air guided weapon (British term).

SAID—Speech autoinstruction device.

SAINT—Satellite inspection technique (Antisatellite system). Satellite intercept.

SAKI—Solartron automatic keyboard instructor (manufactured by Solartron Industrial Controls, Ltd., Farnborough, Hampshire, England).

S-AL—Salt-alum.

SALM—Society of Airline Meteorologists.

SALT—Symbolic algebraic language translator (developed by Autonetics Div., North American Aviation, Inc.).

SAM—Stage assembly and maintenance. Synchronous amplitude modulation. School of Aviation Medicine (Air Force Aerospace Medical Center, Brook Air Force Base, San Antonio, Texas). Surface-to-air missile.

SAMA—Scientific Apparatus Makers' Association.

SAMOS—Satellite antimissile observation system.

SAMPE—Society of Aircraft Materials and Process Engineers.

SAMS—Satellite automonitor system (developed by Control Data Corp.).

SAO—Select address and operate. Smithsonian Astrophysical Observatory (Cambridge, Mass.).

SAOS—Select address and provide output signal.

SAP—Society for Applied Spectroscopy (Boston College, Chestnut Hill 67, Mass.). Symbolic assembly program.

SAR—Search and rescue. Submarine advanced reactor (West Milton, N. Y. and U.S.S. Triton).

SARA—Still another response averager. Sequential automatic recorder and annunciator (automatic process monitor and recorder built by Taller and Cooper).

SARAH—Search and rescue and homing (manufactured by Ultra Electric Ltd., London W.3, England).

SARBE—Search and rescue beacon system (developed by Burndept Ltd., England).

SARPS—Standards and recommended practices.

SARUS—Search and rescue using satellites.

SAS—Shift accumulator left, including sign. Society for Applied Spectroscopy. Stability augmentation system (developed by Boeing).

SASC—Semiautomated stock control.

SASI — Southern Association of Science and Industry.

SASP—Special weapons ordnance points.

SAT—Subscriber access terminal.

SATAF—Site-activation task force (Ballistic Systems Div., U. S. Air Force, Systems Command).

SATAN — Sensor for airborne terrain analysis.

SATCC—Southern Air Traffic Control Centre (Great Britain).

SATCO—Signal automatic air traffic control system (developed by N. V. Hollandse Signaal Apparaten).

SATE—Semiautomatic test equipment (developed by Librascope **Div., General Precision, Inc.).**

SATIN—Sage air traffic integration (project on using SAGE for air traffic control).

SATRAC—Satellite automatic terminal rendezvous and coupling.

SATRACK—Satellite tracking camera.

SATS—Small airfield tactical support.

SATT—Strowger automatic toll ticketing (telephone term). Semiautomatic transistor tester (manufactured by Monitor Systems, Inc., Fort Washington, Pa.).

SAU—Search attack unit.

SAVE—Service Activities of Voluntary Engineers (an IBT Group of volunteers in medical research).

SAVOR—Signal-actuated voice recorder.

SAWE—Society of Aeronautical Weight Engineers.

SB—Slow-burning wire. Stabilized breakdown. Straight binary.

SBA—Small Business Administration.

SBAC—Society of British Aircraft Constructors.

SBC—Small bayonet cap.

SBCC—Separate bias, common control.

SBIC—Small Business Investment Company.

SBR—Styrene-butadiene rubber.

SBS—Straight binary seconds.

SBSC—Separate bias, single control.

SC—Screwed. Sectional center (telephone term). Sequence counter. Signal Corps. Sine-cosine. Stop-continue register. Supervisory control.

S/C—Short circuit.

SCA—Selectively clear accumulator. Subsidiary communications allocation. Subsidiary communications authorization.

SCAMA—Switching conference and monitoring arrangement.

SCAMP—Signal-conditioning amplifier (developed by Neff Instrument Co., Duarte, Calif.). Single-channel amplitude monopulse processing (developed by Sperry Gyroscope Co., Great Neck, L. I., N. Y.).

SCAN—Switched circuit automatic network.

SCAND—Single-crystal automatic neutron diffractometer (developed by Bell Laboratories, Murray Hill, N. J.).

SCANDOC—Scandinavian Documentation Center (2136 P St. N.W., Washington, D. C.).

SCANS—Scheduling control and automation by network systems.

SCAP—Silent, compact auxiliary power (developed by TAPCO Div. of Thompson RAMO Wooldridge for U. S. Army Mobility Command R & D Labs, Ft. Belvoir, Va.).

SCAR—Scandinavian Council for Applied Research (Gaustadalleen 30, Blindern, Norway). Special Committee for Antarctic Research. Sub-caliber aircraft rocket. Submarine celestial altitude recorder (developed by Sperry Piedmont Corp.). Sun-caliber aircraft rocket.

SCARDE—Study Committee on Analysis of Research, Development, and Engineering.

SCAT—South Pacific Combat Air Transport. Special Advisory Committee on Telecommunications. Supersonic commercial air transport.

SCATE—Stromberg-Carlson automatic testing equipment.

SCB—Silver-plated cadmium bronze.

SCC—Satellite control center. Small centre contact. Storage connecting circuit (teletype term).

SCD—Screwed.

SCDSB—Supressed-carrier double sideband.

SCE—Saturated calomel electrode. Schedule compliance evaluation. Solder circuit etch.

SCEPTRON—Spectral comparative pattern recognizer (developed by Sperry Gyroscope Co.).

SCH—Schedule.

SCHO—Standard controlled heterodyne oscillator.

SCHWR—Steam-cooled heavy water reactor.

SCI—Simulation Councils, Inc. Society of the Chemical In- **[Cont.]**

dustry (British).

SCL—Scale. Selectively cross-linked (heat-shrinkable tubing). Space-charge-limited. Symmetric clipper.

SCLC—Space-charge-limited currents.

SCM—Selective complement accumulator.

SCMA—Southern California Meter Association.

SCNA—Sudden cosmic noise absorption.

SCO—Subcarrier oscillator.

SCODA—Scan coherent doppler attachment.

SCOPE—Sequential customer order processing electronically. Stromberg central operations panel—electric (manufactured by Stromberg Time Corp.). System to coordinate the operation of peripheral equipment (developed by Minneapolis - Honeywell, Computer Div.).

SCOPT—Subcommittee on programming technology.

SCOR — Special Committee on Oceanic Research (set up by ICSU).

SCORE—Satellite computer-operated readiness equipment. Signal communication by orbiting relay experiment.

SCOT — Supplementary checkout trailer.

SCOTICE—Scotland-Iceland telephone cable.

scp—Spherical candlepower.

SCR—Series control relay (JIC and NMTBA term). Silicon controlled rectifier.

SCRA—Stanford Center for Radar Astronomy.

SCRAM—Selective combat - range artillery missile (developed by The Martin Co.).

SCS—Single-channel simplex.

SCTL—Short-circuited transmission line.

SCUBA—Self-contained underwater breathing apparatus.

SCUDS—Simplification, clarification, unification, decimalization, standardization.

SD—Sample delay. Secretary of Defense. Seize detector. Service drop cable. Slow down (JIC and NMTBA term). Spectral distribution. Standard deviation. Stereo-directional. Steward (U. S. Navy). Superintendent of Documents. Surveillance drone.

SDA — Symbols-digits-alphabetics. Systems dynamic analyzer.

SDAP—Systems development analysis program.

SDB—Square die bushing.

SDC—Shaft position-to-digital converter. Signal data converter. Stabilization data computers (developed by Burroughs for use on Polaris submarines). Seize-detector control.

SDF—Self - defense force (Japan's Army, Air Force, and Navy). Single degree of freedom. Spectral density function. Static direction finder.

SDGA—Single - conductor, degaussing, armored cable.

SDHE—Spacecraft data - handling equipment.

SDI—Selective dissemination of information (IBM system).

SDM—Somadendrite membrane.

SDR—Self-decoding readout. Snap development reactor. Sodium-deuterium reactor. System development requirement.

SDSBE—San Diego Symposium for Biomedical Engineering.

SDT—Scientific distribution technique.

SDTK — Supported drift-tube klystron.

SDU—Spectrum display unit. Subcarrier delay unit.

SDV—Slowed-down video.

SE—Service entrance cable, unprotected type. Starter electrode.

Se—Set.

S & E—Surveillance and entry.

SEA—Subterranean Exploration Agency. Sudden enhancement of atmospherics.

SEAC—Standards Eastern automatic computer (digital computer completed by National Bureau of Standards in May, 1950).

SEADAC—Seakeeping Data Analysis Center (David Taylor Model Basin).

SEATO—Southeast Asia Treaty Organization.

SEB—Southern Electricity Board (British electrical power agency).

SEC—Secondary.

SECAIR—Secretary of the Air Force.

SECO—Self-regulating error-correcting coder-decoder (developed by Lincoln Labs, Massachusetts Institute of Technology, Cambridge, Mass.). Sequential control (teletype term). Sustainer engine cutoff.

SECOR—Sequential collation of range (geodetic equipment for transit satellite developed by Cubic Corp.).

SEDA—State Emergency Defense Airlift.

SEE—Society of Environmental Engineers (British engineering society).

SEEB — Southeastern Electricity Board (British electrical power agency).

SEF—Shielding effectiveness factor.

SEFAR—Sonic end fire for azimuth and range.

SEIC—Solar Energy Information Center (U. S. Army Signal Research and Development Laboratory, Ft. Monmouth, N. J.).

SELCAL—Selective calling.

SEMO—Systems Engineering Management Organization (NATO group).

SEP—Polish Association of Engineers. Slug ejector punch.

SEPR—Societé de'Etude de la Propulsion par Reaction (Paris, France).

SEQUR—Safety equipment requirements.

SER—SNAP 2 experimental reactor.

SERF—Sandia engineering reactor facility.

SERL—Services Electronics Research Laboratory (British government research and development lab).

SERME—Sign error root modulus error.

SERT—Space electric rocket test (manufactured by RCA Astro-Electronics Div.).

SES—Small Edison screw. Standards Engineers Society.

SESA—Signal Equipment Support Agency (U. S. Army Signal Corps, Ft. Monmouth, N. J.). Society for Experimental Stress Analysis (21 Bridge Square, Westport, Mass.).

SET—Solar energy thermionic conversion system (NASA program being developed by Electro-Optical Systems, Inc.).

SETA—Simplified electronic tracking apparatus.

SETAF—Southern Europe Task Force.

SETAR—Serial event timer and recorder.

SETC—Solid electrolyte tantalum capacitor.

SETP—Society of Experimental Test Pilots.

SEV—Schweizerischer Elek- **[Cont.]**

trotechnischer Verein (Swiss organization).

SF—Safety factor. Semifinished. Shift forward. Silicone rubber-insulated fixture wire, solid or 7-strand. Single frequency. Standard frequency transmission. Structure function. Success factor (value analysis term).

S/F—Store-and-forward.

SFC—Space flight center. Surface.

SFD—Straightforward. Systems flexowriter double case.

SFE—Societé Francaise des Electriciens.

SFF—Silicone rubber-insulated fixture wire, flexible stranding.

SFM — Simulated flow method. Swept-frequency modulation.

SFOC—Space Flight Operations Center (Jet Propulsion Labs, Pasadena, Calif.).

SFOF—Space Flight Operation Facility.

SFP—Straight fixed price.

SFR—Submarine fleet reactor.

SFRJ—Solid-fuel ramjet.

SFS—Saybolt furol seconds (time units referring to the Saybolt viscometer with a furol capillary).

SFSA—Steel Founders' Society of America (606 Terminal Tower, Cleveland 13, Ohio).

SG—Scanning gate. Screen grid. Set gate. Symbol generator.

SGACC—Secrétariat Général de l'-Aviation Civile et Commerciale (French Government Agency similar to U. S. FAA).

SGCS—Silicon gate-controlled switch.

SGL—Signal.

SGM—Spark-gap modulator.

SGN—Scan gate number.

SGR—Sodium-cooled graphite-moderated reactor.

SH—Sequence history. Shell. Shift. Sulfhydryls (antiradiation com-

pounds).

SHAPE — Supreme Headquarters, Allied Powers in Europe.

S-HEMP—System—hydraulic, electrical, mechanical, pneumatic.

SHF—Super high frequency (3000-30,000 megacycles).

SHFA—Single-conductor, heat- and flame-resistant armored cable.

SHOF—Shipboard cable, heat- and oil-resistant, flexible.

SHORAN—Short-range navigation.

SHP—Standard holding procedure (CAA term).

SI—Sample interval. Screen-grid input. Seal-in relay. Semi-insulating. Special instruction (telephone term). Spectrum index. Speed indicator. Systéme International d'-Unites (international system of units).

S/I—Signal-to-intermodulation ratio.

SIA—Strategic Industries Association.

SIAP—Straight-in approach (CAA term).

SIB—Sociedade Interplanetaria Brasileira (Caixa Postal 6450, Sas Paulo, Brazil).

SIBS—Stellar inertial bombing system (manufactured by AC Spark Plug, Milwaukee, Wis.; began in 1955).

SIC—Specific inductive capacity. Standard industrial classification. Standard Industrial Code).

SID—Standard instrument departure. Sudden ionospheric disturbance.

SIE—Science and information exchange.

SIF—Secure identification feature. Selective identification feature.

SIFT—Share internal Fortran translator. Simplified input for Toss (IBM-7090 code program).

SIG—Signal.

SIL—Speech interference level. Surge impedance loading.

SILS—Shipboard impact locator system.

SIM—Simulated approach.

SIMA—Scientific Instrument Manufacturers' Association of Great Britain (20 Queen Anne St., London W.1, England).

SIMAJ—Scientific Instrument Manufacturers' Association of Japan.

SIMCON—Simplified control.

SIMFAC—Simulation facility (built for SAC by ITT).

SIMPAC—Simulation package (developed by Systems Development Corp.).

SINPO—Signal strength, interference, noise, fading, quality.

SINS—Ship's inertial navigation system.

SIO—Scripps Institution of Oceanography.

SIP—Short irregular pulses.

SIPRE—Snow, ice, and permafrost research establishment (U. S. Army Engineers Headquarters, 825 Emerson St., Evanston, Ill.).

SIR—Submarine intermediate reactor.

SIRSA—Special Industrial Radio Service Association (G. Kenneth Adams, Exec. Secy., Room 813, Sheraton Bldg., 711 14th St. N.W., Washington, D. C.).

SISP—Sudden increases of solar particles.

SISS—Submarine integrated sonar system.

SIT—Society of Instrument Technology (British organization—20 Queen Anne St., London W.1, England).

SIT-REP—Situation report.

SJ—300-volt junior service portable cord.

SJCC—Spring joint computer conference.

SJO—Junior hard-service cord (oil-resistant).

SJT—Junior hard-service cord (thermoplastic).

SKED—Schedule.

SKM—Sine-cosine multiplier.

SKP—Skip.

SKYIR—Sky fire fighting.

SL—Sea level. Silicone lacquer. Swagelok.

S & L—Systems and logistics.

SLA—Special Libraries Association.

SLAD—Select ADC and increment.

SLAG—Safe launch angle gate.

SLAM—Supersonic low-altitude missile (U. S. Air Force). Surface-to-surface low-altitude missile.

SLAR—Select ADC register. Side-looking airborne radar.

SLATE—Small lightweight altitude transmission equipment (or transponder).

SLBM—Space - launched ballistic missiles.

SLC—Searchlight control radar. Straight-line capacity. Subscriber line circuit (telephone term).

SLCS—Select contact sense.

SLD—Solid.

SLEW—Static load error washout (developed by Moog Servocontrols, Inc.).

SLF—Straight-line frequency. Symmetric filter.

SLGM — Surface - launched guided missile.

SLM—Ship-launched missile.

SLME—Select manual entry switches.

SLOMAR—Space logistics, maintenance, and repair. Space logistic maintenance and rescue vehicle.

SLRAP—Standard low - frequency range approach.

SLRN—Select read numerically.

SLS—Side-lobe suppression.

SL ST—Slightly staining.

SLTA—Select TAS.

SLTF—Silo launch test facility.

SLURREX—Slurry reactor experiment.

SLV—Satellite launching vehicle. Space launch vehicle. Standard launch vehicle.

SLW—Straight-line wavelength.

SM—Strategic missile. Submarine minelayer (U. S. Navy). Superimpose.

SMA—Squadron maintenance area.

SMAB—Solid motor assembly building.

SMAC—Submicron aerosol collector.

SMAMA—Sacramento Air Materiel Area (McClellan Air Force Base, Sacramento, Calif.).

SMART—Satellite maintenance and repair techniques. Sequential mechanism for automatic recording and testing (semiconductor tester, developed by Texas Instruments). Space maintenance and repair techniques. Supersonic military air research track (Hurricane Mesa, Utah). System malfunction analysis reinforcement trainer (developed by North American Electronic Systems, Inc., Norristown, Pa.).

SMC—Scientific Manpower Commission.

SMH—Simple harmonic motion.

smi—Statute miles.

SMIT—Spin motor interruption technique.

SMITE—Simulation model of interceptor terminal effectiveness.

SML—Symbolic machine language.

SMP—Sampler.

SMPTE—Society of Motion Picture and TV Engineers.

SMS — Semiconductor-metal-semiconductor. Ship's-motion simulator. Standard modular system.

Strategic Missiles Squadron. Synchronous-altitude meteorological satellite.

SMT—Small missile telecamera.

SMU—Self-maneuvering unit (space pack developed by Ling-Temco-Vought, Dallas, Texas).

SMV—Satellite mutual visibility.

SMW—Strategic Missile Wing (part of Strategic Air Command).

SMX—Sub-multiplexer unit.

SN—Sign.

S/N—Signal-to-noise.

SNAC—Sonar automatic controller.

SNAME—Society of Naval Architects and Marine Engineers (74 Trinity Place, New York 6, N.Y.).

SNAP—Simplified numerical automatic programmer (developed by Brown & Sharpe Mfg. Co.). Systems for nuclear auxiliary power (developed by The Martin Co.).

SNAPTRAN—Snap transient (AEC tests at Idaho Falls, Idaho).

SND-MB—Selected natural diamond-metal bond.

SNI—Sequence-number indicator.

SNIRD—Supposedly noiseless infrared detector.

SNL—Standard nomenclaure list.

SNO—Serial number.

SNORT—Supersonic naval ordnance research track.

SNP—Synchro null pulses.

SNPO—Space Nuclear Propulsion Office.

SNPOA—Space Nuclear Propulsion Office, Albuquerque, N. Mex.

SNPOC—Space Nuclear Propulsion Office, Cleveland, Ohio.

SNPON—Space Nuclear Propulsion Office, Nevada.

SNR—Signal-to-noise ratio.

SNT—Society for Nondestructive Testing.

SO—Spring opening (switch). Surveillance Officer. 600-volt, senior service, neoprene jacket, portable cord.

S/O—Send only.

SOA—State of the art (reliability term).

SOC—Satellite orbit control. Sector Operation Center. Socket (JIC and NMTBA term).

SOCOM—Solar Optical Communications System (solar radiation system developed by Electro-Optical Systems). Solar orbital communications.

SOEP—Solar-oriented experiment package.

SOFAR—Sound fixing and ranging.

S/OFF—Sign-off.

SOL—Solenoid (JIC and NMTBA term). Soluble. Systems-oriented language.

SOLARIS—Submerged-object locating and retrieving identification system (antisubmarine warfare device designed by Vitro Labs).

SOLN—Solution.

SOLO—Selective optical lock-on (developed by Chicago Aerial Industries).

SOLOMON—Simultaneous operation linked ordinal modular network parallel-network computer developed by Westinghouse Electric Corp., Baltimore, Md.).

SOM—Start of message.

S/ON—Sign-on.

SONAR—Sound navigation and ranging.

SONOAN—Sonic noise analyzer.

SOP—Standard operating procedure.

SOPA—Senior officer present afloat.

SOR—Specific operational requirement. Systems operations recommendation.

SORAP—Standard omni-range approach.

SORD—Society of Record Dealers of America.

SORTE—Summary of radiation-tolerant electronics (file of data on the effects of radiation on components developed by Bendix Systems Div., Ann Arbor, Mich.).

SORTI—Star - oriented real - time tracking instrument (missile tracking system).

SORTIE—Super - orbital re-entry test integrated environment (U. S. Air Force glide entry vehicle).

SOS—Congress of Scientists on Survival. Service of Supply. Share operating system.

SOSU—Scout Observation Service Unit.

SOTA—State of the art.

SOTIM—Sonic observation of the trajectory and impact on missiles.

SOTUS—Sequentially operated teletypewriter universal selector.

SP—All-rubber parallel cord. Self-powered. Shift pulses. Shore patrol. Silver plate. Special projects. Splash plate (rocket term). Square punch. Standard pile. Static pressure. Submarine patrol.

SPA—Single-position automatic tester (devdeloped by Philco Corp.). Subject to partial average. Systems and Procedures Association (817 Penobscot Bldg., Detroit 26, Mich.).

SPAA—Systems and Procedures Association of America (4463 Penobscot Bldg., Detroit 26, Mich.).

SPAC—Spatial computer (Bell Labs).

SPACE—Self - programming automatic circuit evaluator (developed by Brooks Research, Inc., East Rochester, N.Y.). Space contact. Space Program American Citizens' Effort, Inc. (19 W. 44th St., New York 36, N. Y.).

SPACON—Space Control.

SPAD—Space-based missile defense (project code name for ARPA—Air Force "Defender" missile defense program).

SPADATS—Space detection and tracking system.

SPALT—Special projects alteration.

SPANDAR—Space range radar (developed by Raytheon).

SpaN NET—Space navigation network.

SPANRAD—Superimposed panoramic radar display (U.S. Navy device—converts radar picture to a TV picture—built by Intercontinental Electronics Corp.).

SPAR—Seagoing platform for acoustic research (developed by U. S. Naval Ordnance Laboratory).

SPARTA—Sequential programmed automatic recording transistor analyzer.

SPASUR—Space surveillance system.

SPAT—Silicon precision alloy transistor.

SPATE—Sergeant production automatic test equipment.

SPC—Silver-plated copper. Specific propellant consumption.

SPCC—Ship's parts control center.

SPCN—Silver - plated copperweld conductor.

SPD—System program director. Systems programmatic double case.

SPDT—Single-pole double-throw.

SPE—Shift preserving sign, extracting. Society of Plastics Engineers (65 Prospect St., Stamford, Conn.). Stored program element.

SPEARS—Satellite photoelectronic analog rectification system (developed by Image Instruments, Inc., Newton, Mass., for Tiros satellite project).

SPEC—Specification. Stored program educational computer (manufactured by Computer Control Co., Inc.).

SPEDAC—Solid-state parallel expandable differential analyzer computer (developed by Hazeltine

Technical Development Center, Indianapolis).

SPEDTAR—Stored program educational transistorized automatic computer (developed by Oregon College of Education).

SPERT—Special power excursion reactor test.

SPF—Spectrophotofluorometer. Syntactic phenolic foam.

SPFW—Single-phase full-wave.

SP/GR—Specific gravity.

SP-HL—Sun present—horizon lost.

SPHT—Super pressure—high temperature.

SP/HT—Specific heat.

SPHW—Single-phase half-wave.

SPI—Society of the Plastics Industry.

SPIA—Solid Propellant Information Agency (operated by Applied Physics Laboratory, Johns Hopkins University, Silver Spring, Md.).

SPIE—Society of Photographic Instrumentation Engineers (P.O. Box 288, Redondo Beach, Calif.).

SPIRAL—Sperry inertial radar altimeter.

SPIRE—Spatial inertial reference equipment (inertial guidance equipment for aircraft developed by MIT).

SPIT—Selective printing of items from tape (developed by Associated Consultants, Philadelphia, Pa.).

SPKR—Speaker.

SPL—Sound pressure level. Special. Speed-phase lock.

SPLIT—Sundstrand processing language internally translated.

SPM—Spectrophosphorimeter.

SPO—Short-period oscillations. Special Projects Office (U. S. Navy). System Program Offices.

SPOOK—Supervisory program over other kinds (program for the IBM 7090 computer enabling it to monitor its own operations).

SPR—Sequential probability ratio (a statistical test for reliability). SE-pulse readout. Solid-propellant rocket. Sudden-pressure relay. System performance rating.

SPRF—Sandia Pulsed Reactor Facility (Albuquerque, N. Mex.).

SPRINT—Selective printer.

SPS—Shift preserving sign, substituting. Space power system. Symbolic programming systems. Systems programmatic single case.

SPSE—Society of Photographic Scientists and Engineers.

SPST—Single-pole single-throw.

SPT—Society of Phototechnologists. All-plastic parallel cord.

SPU—Subsurface propulsion unit.

SPUD—Stored program universal demonstrator (developed by BTL for teaching computers).

SPUNFIT—Space union and fitting wrench.

SPUR—Space power unit reactor (U. S. Air Force).

SPURT—Small primate unrestrained test.

SPWG—Space parts working group.

SQA—Squaring amplifier.

SQAT—Shipboard qualification assistance team.

SQC—Statistical quality control.

SQDN—Squadron.

SQT—Square rooter.

SR—Range cable (rubber). Saturable reactor. Search and rescue. Sensitivity ratio. Shift register. Shift reverse. Silicon rectifier. Silicone rubber. Solar radiation. Solid rocket. Speed regulator. State register. Study requirement. Subscriber register. Sunrise.

S/R—Send or receive.

SRAM—Some remarks on abstract machines.

SRAP—Standard Range Approach (CAA term).

SRBM—Short-range ballistic missile.

SRCH—Search.

SRE—Society of Relay Engineers (British). Sodium reactor experiment (Santa Susana, Calif.).

SRF—Self-resonant frequency. Semi-reinforcing furnace.

SRG—Short range.

SRHV—2500-volt insulated hookup wire.

SRI—Servo repeater indicator. Stanford Research Institute.

SRLD—Small rocket lift device.

SRML—Short-range missile launcher.

SRO—Society of Radio Operators. Supervisor of Range Operations.

SRP—Seat reference point. Standard relative power.

SRPO—Science Resources Planning Office (National Science Foundation).

SRR—Search and range radar. Short-range radar.

SRRF—1000 - volt radio - frequency wire.

SRS—Submarine reactor, small.

S-RS—Short-range search.

SRT—Range cable (thermoplastic). Synchro and resolver transmission.

SRTF—Short-range task force (developed initial specifications for COBOL computer language).

SS—Selective signaling. Selector, or transfer switch (JIC term). Sequence switch. Set steering. Single shot. Small signal. Solid state. Stainless steel. Statistical standards. Steamship. Submarine (U. S. Navy). Sunset. Surface-to-surface. Synchro standard.

SSA—Signal Supply Agency. Synchro signal amplifier.

SSB—Single-sideband.

SSBARA—Single-sideband Amateur Radio Association.

SSB(N)—Ship, submarine, [Cont.]

ballistic (nuclear-powered).

SSBS—Sol Sol Balistique Strategique.

SSBSC—Single-sideband suppressed carrier.

SSBSCOM—Single - sideband suppressed-carrier optical modulator.

SSC — Southeastern Simulation Council.

SSCC—Space Surveillance Control Center.

SSCR—Spectral Shift Control Reactor.

SSD—Seize - signal detector. Sequence switch driver (telephone term). Space Systems Division U. S. Air Force Systems Command).

SSDR—Satellite situation display room.

SSE—Self-sustained emission (tube).

SSEC—Selective sequence electronic calculator.

SSF—Saybolt seconds furol (unit of viscosity).

SSFL—Steady-state Fermi level.

SSGA—Single-conductor, shipboard general use, armored cable.

SSGN—Submarine, guided-missile, nuclear.

SSL—Shift and select.

SSLT—Solid-state logic timer.

SSM—Subsynaptic membrane. Surface-to-surface missile.

SSMS—Solid-state mass spectrometer.

SS(N)—Nuclear-powered submarine (U. S. Navy).

SSO—Space Station Office (NASA's Langley Research Center). System Staff Offices. Submarine Supply Office.

SSP—Solid-state pneumatics. Steam service pressure.

SS POLY—Semisolid polyethylene.

SSR—Secondary surveillance radar. Static oscillation squelch range.

S-S R—Ship-shape radar.

SSRC—Spectral shift control reactor.

SSRN—Submarine, radar, nuclear.

SSSC—Single - sideband suppressed carrier. Special Spectrum Study Committee (EIA).

SST—Sea surface temperature. Supersonic transport.

SS TEF—Semisolid Teflon.

SSU—Seconds Saybolt universal (unit of viscosity).

S-SV—Static self-verification.

SSW—Safety switch (JIC and NM-TBA term).

ST—Scalar totalizer. Schmitt trigger. Screw terminals. Set trigger. Staining. Stagnation region. Standard time. Start. Start timing. Stranded. Studio to transmitter. 600-volt, junior service, vinyl, portable cord.

STA—Special temporary authorization. Station to station. Store accumulator.

STAB AMP—Stabilizing amplifier.

STAG—Strategy and Tactics Analysis Group (U. S. Army, Bethesda, Md.).

STALO—Stabilized local oscillator.

STAR—Safe teen-age rocketry (first U. S. Army Program. Simultaneous temperature alarm readout (manufactured by Fischer & Porter). Space technology and advanced research. Space thermionic auxiliary reactor (General Electric space power plant). Special tube analyzing recorder (developed by IBM). Specialized training and reassignment (U. S. Army).

STARCOM—Strategic Army Communications Network.

STARS—Satellite Telemetry Automatic Reduction System.

STBL—Stable.

STC—Satellite Test Center. Sensitivity time control.

STD—Standard. Subscriber trunk

dialing (telephone term).

STEDI—Space thrust evaluation and disposal investigation (Boeing Co. study of antisatellite weapon).

STEM—Stored tubular extensible member.

STEP—Simple transition to electronic processing.

STEPS—Solar thermionic electric power system (built by General Electric for Air Force). Solar thermionic electrical propulsion systems.

STF—Space track facility.

STG—Space Task Group (NASA agency).

STIAP—Standard instrument approach.

STINGS—Stellar inertial guidance system (U. S. Air Force project).

STL—Sequential table lockup. Studio-transmitter-link.

STLO—Scientific and **Technical** Liaison Office (U. S. Air Force).

STLT—Studio-transmitter link-TV.

STMGR—Station manager.

STN—Station.

STOL—Short takeoff and landing.

STOR—Store.

STP—Seattle test program (developed by Boeing; Minuteman missile launch complex at Seattle, Wash.). Stop. Standard temperature and pressure. Systems training program (Air Defense Command).

STR—Store. Submarine thermal reactor (developed by Westinghouse).

STRAD—Switching, transmitting, receiving, and distribution system (developed by Standard Telephones & Cables to handle telegraph messages for air traffic control).

STRADAP—Storm radar data processor.

STRAC—Strategic Army Corps.

STRAP—Stretch assembly program (for IBM "Stretch" computer).

STRATCOM—Strategic Communication System (U. S. Air Force).

STRATCOM MEX — Strategic Communications Military Exchange.

STS—Static test stand. Supersonic target systems.

STTA—Technical Air Telecommunications Service (French Ministry of the Air).

STU—Submersible test unit.

STV—Separation test vehicle.

STWE—Society of Technical Writers and Editors.

SU—Strontium units.

SUB—Subtract.

SUBIC—Submarine integrated control (Army-Navy instrumentation program supervised by Office of Naval Research and BuShips; coordinator is Electric Boat Co.).

SUBROC—Submarine rocket.

SUE—Strontium unit equivalent. Sudden expansion (environmental tester developed by Marquardt Corp.).

SUIAP—Simplified unit invoice accounting plan system.

SUM—Surface-to-underwater missile.

SUN—Symbols, units, and nomenclature.

SUP—Suppressor.

SUPER—Superheterodyne.

SUPO—Superpower.

SURANO—Surface radar and navigation operation (developed by Raytheon).

SURCAL—Space surveillance system calibration (U. S. satellite program).

SURE—Symbolic utilities revenue environment (IBM computer program for public utilities).

SURIC—Surface integrated control (Army-Navy **instrumentation pro-**

gram supervised by Office of Naval Research and BuShips; coordinator is Sperry-Rand).

SUS—Saybolt universal seconds (time units referring to the Saybolt viscometer).

SUTEC—Seneca Lake Underwater Test and Evaluation Center (Dresden, N. Y.).

SV—Secondary valve. Self-verification. Set value. Silicone varnish. Vacuum-cleaner cord (rubber).

SVC—Service.

SVE—Swept volume efficiency (an antenna system developed by General Bronze Co.).

SVEA—Scioto Valley Electric Association (1329 Galena Park, Portsmouth, Ohio).

SVO—Vacuum-cleaner cord, neoprene jacket.

SVS—Stationary control variable speed.

SVT—Vacuum-cleaner cord, plastic jacket.

SVTP—Sound velocity temperature, pressure instrument.

SW—Beam-switching tube. Secretary of War. Shortwave. Socket weld.

SWAC—Standards Western automatic computer (U. S. National Bureau of Standards).

SWAMI—Standing-wave area motion indicator.

SWD—Smaller word.

SWE—Shift word, extracting. Society of Women Engineers.

SWEB—South Wales Electricity Board (British electrical power agency).

SWEE—Southwest Electronic Exhibit.

SWFC—Surface Weapons Fire Control (U. S. Navy Bureau for Research).

SWI—Special World Intervals (IGY term). Stall warning indicator.

SWIRECO—Southwestern Regional Conference of the Institute of Radio Engineers.

SWL—Short wavelength limit. Shortwave listener.

SWR—Standing-wave ratio.

SWS—Shift word, substituting.

SWTL—Surface wave transmission line.

SX—Simplex (telephone signaling system).

SXN—Section.

SY—Synchronized.

SYCATE—Symptom cause test.

SYLATINS—Symbolic Analysis Technique for Information Systems.

SYM—Symmetrical. System.

SYMPAC—Symbolic program for automatic control (developed by UNIVAC Div., Sperry-Rand Corp.).

SYNTAC—Synthetic tactics (operations research term).

SYSEC—System synthesizer and evaluation center.

SYSTO—System Staff Office.

SZ—Size.

T

T—Target. Tesla (weber/meter^2). Thermoplastic-insulated lead wire. Thrust. Transformer. Transmitting. Trigger. Triode. True (bearing). Tubular (pilot bulb designation.

TA—Switchboard wire, thermoplastic and felted asbestos insulation. Tape adapter. Target.

TAA—Television Appliance Association (424 Failing Bldg., Portland, Ore.).

TAB—Tabulate switch. Technical Assistance Board (United Nations).

TABSOL—Tabular systems-oriented language (developed by General Electric).

TABSTONE—Target and background signal-to-noise experiments.

TABWAG—Tank battle war game.

TAC—Tactical. Tactical Air Command. Technical Area Coordinator. Technical Assistance Committee (United Nations). Tracking accuracy control. Transformer analog computer. Translator assembler-compiler (computer term). Transistorized automatic control.

TACAN—Tactical air navigation.

TACC—Tactical Air Control Center.

TACT—Transistor and component tester (developed by Texas Instruments, Inc.).

TAD—Target acquisition data.

TADIC—Telemetry analog-to-digital information converter (developed by EMI Electronics, Ltd., England).

TAD/P—Terminal area distribution processing.

TADS—Teletypewriter automatic dispatch system.

TAG—Test automation growth. The Adjutant General.

TAGA—Technical Association of the Graphic Arts.

TAHA—Tapered aperture horn antenna (developed for U.S. Army Signal R & D Laboratory by Developmental Engineering Corp.).

TAJ—Thermal arc jet.

TAM—Tangent approximating manifold. Technical Area Manager.

TAMCO—Training aid for MOBIDIC console operators (developed

by Sylvania Electric Products, Needham, Mass.).

TAOC—Tactical Air Operations Center.

TAP—Terrestrial auxiliary power (remote-location generator designed by Westinghouse for the Air Force).

TAPAC—Tape automatic positioning and control.

TAPE—Tape automatic preparation equipment (developed by McDonnell Aircraft).

TAPPI—Technical Association of the Pulp and Paper Industry.

TAR—Terrain-avoidance radar (developed by General Dynamics, San Diego, Calif.). Training-Administration Reserve (U.S. Navy). Track address register (magnetic storage drum).

TARAN—Tactical attack radar and navigator (developed by Hughes Aircraft Co.).

TARC—Television Allocation Research Committee. Television Allocation Research Council.

TARE—Transistor analysis recording equipment.

TARGET—Thermal advanced reactor, gas-cooled, exploiting thorium.

TARS—Three-axis reference system (developed by Minneapolis-Honeywell).

TAS—Target acquisition system. Telephone answering service. Terminal address selector. True air speed.

TASC—Terminal area sequencing and control.

TASCON—Television automatic sequence control (computer developed by Thompson-Ramo-Wooldridge for TV station KNXT, Los Angeles).

TASI—Time assignment speech interpolation (a high-speed transmission and switching system for telephone, using idle time during a call to interpolate additional calls).

TASO—Television Allocations Study Organization.

TAT—Thrust-augmented Thor.

TATSA—Transportation Aircraft Test and Support Activity (Ft. Rucker, Ala.).

TAVE—Thor-Agena vibration experiment.

TAVET—Temperature acceleration vibration environmental tester (developed by AVCO).

TAW—Tactical assault weapon.

TAWCS—Tactical air weapons control system (radar system manufactured by Hughes Aircraft, Fullerton, Calif.).

TAWS—Thomasville Aircraft and Warning Station (Thomasville, Ala.).

TB—Tangential bracket. Technical bulletin. Terminal block. Terminal board (JIC and NMTBA term). Trial balloon.

TBC—Trunk block connector.

TBGAA—Travel by government automobile authorized.

TBI—Threaded blind inserts.

TBM—Tactical Ballistic Missile.

TBMAA—Travel by military aircraft authorized.

TBMX—Tactical ballistic missile experiment.

TBO—Time between overhauls.

TBP—Twisted bonded pair.

TBS—Talk between ships. Translator bail switch.

TBWP—Triple-braid weatherproof conductors.

TBX—Tactical-range ballistic missile.

TC—Temperature controller. Test controller. Thermocouple. Time to computation. Tinned copper. Toll

center (telephone term). Toll completing. Transistorized carrier. Transportation Corps.

Tc—Curie point or Curie temperature.

tc—Teracycle.

T & C—Targeting and control. Time and charges (telephone term).

TCBV—Temperature coefficient of breakdown voltage.

TCC—Television control center. Temperature coefficient of capacitance. Traffic control center. Troop Carrier Command.

TCCOT—Chief of Transportation (U.S. Army).

TCE—Total composite error.

TCEA—Training center for experimental aerodynamics (NATO educational institution—Rhode-Saint-Genese, Belgium).

TCEP—Tris (beta chloroethyl) phosphate (flameproofing agent).

TCEWA—Twin Cities Electronic Wholesalers' Association.

TCI—Terrain-clearance indicator. Trunk cut in.

TCL—Transistor-coupled logic.

TCM—Telemetry code modulation. Terminal-to-computer multiplexer. Translator cam magnet.

TCMA—Tabulating Card Manufacturers' Association.

TCNQ—Tetracyanoquinodimethane (low-resistivity organic material).

TCO—Time and charges, operate (telephone term). Trunk cutoff.

TCPC—Tab card punch control.

TCR—Temperature coefficient of resistance.

TCRE — Temperature-compensated reference element.

TCS—Temporary change of station (U.S. Army). Tone call squelch.

TCT—Tool change time.

TCU—Torpedo Control Unit.

TCW—Time code word. Tinned

copper-weld.

TCWG—Telecommunications working group.

TD—Tank destroyer. Technical data. Time delay. Time difference. Transmitter distributor. Treasury Department. Tunnel diode.

T/D—Tons per day.

T & D—Transmission and distribution.

TDC—Training Device Center (U.S. Navy). Top dead center.

TDDL—Time division data link.

TDE—Time displacement error.

TDEC—Technical Development Evaluation Center (CAA installation at Indianapolis).

TDF—Two degrees of freedom.

TDH—Total dynamic head.

TDI—Toluene diisocyanate (used for treating *Mylar*).

TDM—Time-division-multiplex.

TDMS—Telegraph distortion measuring system.

TDP—Traffic data processing. Tele-data processing.

TDPFO—Temporary duty pending further orders (U.S. Army).

TDR—Time-delay relay.

TDS—Tactical data system. Time-division switching. Transistor display and data handling system (developed by Decca Radar, Ltd., London, England).

TDTL—Tunnel diode-transistor logic.

TDY—Temporary duty.

TE—Teleman (U.S. Navy). Topographical engineer. Trailing edge. Tuning eye.

TEA—Texas Electronics Association, Inc.

TEAM—The Lelectronic Association of Missouri.

TEEPEE—Thaler's Project (a long-range radar project under direction of Dr. Wm. J. Thaler of ONR).

TEFC—Totally enclosed fan-cooled (brake motor term).

TEG—Test element group. Thermoelectric generator.

TEI—Transfer on error-indication.

TEL—Transporter-erector-launcher (part of the "Pershing" weapon system built by Thompson-Ramo-Wooldridge). Tetraethyl lead.

TELCO—Telephone company.

TELERAN—Television radar navigation.

TELEX—American Cable and Radio System's International Teleprinter Exchange Service.

TELRY—Telegraph reply.

TELTRAC—Telemetry tracking system (developed by Canoga Electronics Corp.).

TENOC—Ten years in oceanography (U.S. Navy project).

TES—Tidal electric station.

TESA—Television and Electronics Service Association.

TESTS—Technical-Engineering-Science Training for Secretaries.

TETRA—Terminal trajectory telescope.

TETRAC—Tension truss antenna concept (developed by Narmco Mfg. Co.; manufactured by Telecomputing Corp. for the U.S. Naval Electronics Lab).

TEW—Tactical early warning.

TEX—RCA International Teleprinter Exchange Service.

TF—Task Force. Thermoplastic-covered fixture wire—solid or stranded. Thin film.

Tf—Transfer.

TFC—Traffic.

TFCS—Torpedo fire control system.

TFE—Tetrafluoroethylene (fluorocarbon resin).

TFF—Thermoplastic-covered fixture wire—flexible stranding.

TFL—Transient fault locator.

TFR—Television film re-   **[Cont.]**

corder. Tubular flow reactor.

TFT—Thin-film technique. Thin-film technology. Thin-film transistor.

TG—Tape gauge. Trigger.

TGA—Thermogravimetric analysis.

TGL—Triangular guide line.

TGTP—Tuned grid-tuned plate.

THD—Total harmonic distortion.

THFR—Three-conductor, heat- and flame-resistant radio cable.

THI—Temperature-humidity index (meteorological term).

THL—Tuned hybrid lattice.

THOF—Triple-conductor, heat-, oil-, and flame-resistant.

THOR—Transistorized high-speed operations recorder (developed by Panellit).

THS—Thermostat switch (JIC term).

THY—Thyratron.

TI—Temperature indicator.

TIC—Target intercept computer.

TIF—Technical information file. Telephone influence factor. True involute form (a diameter in gear calculations).

TIG—Tungsten inert gas.

TILL—Total initial lamp lumens.

TIM—Temperature indicator monitor. Time-interval measurement. Time-interval meter.

TIMA—Technical Illustrator's Management Association.

TIMM—Thermionic integrated micromodule (developed by General Electric Receiving Tube Department).

TIMS—The Institute for Management Sciences.

TINS—Trains inertial navigation system.

TIO—TV Information Office (666 5th Ave., New York 19, N.Y.). Transistorized image-orthicon camera.

TIR—Total indicator reading. Total-

internal-reflecting.

TIROS—Television, infrared, observation satellite.

TIS—Temperature-indicating switch. Test instrumentation system.

TIT—Turbine inlet temperature.

TKOF—Takeoff.

TKW—Thermal kilowatts.

TL—Time limit. Transmission level. Transmission line.

TLC—Thin-layer chromatography.

TLFO—Telephone.

TLR—Toll line release (telephone term).

TLU—Threshold logic unit.

TLZ—Transfer on less than zero.

T²L—Transistor-transistor logic.

TM—Magnetic tape module. Tactical missile. Tactical monitors. Tangent mechanism. Technical manual. Telemetering. Torpedoman (U.S. Navy). Traffic Manager. Translator code magnet. Turbine flow meter.

T-M—Time and materials.

TME—Technische Mass Einheit (Engineering Mass Unit).

TMF—Time marker frequency.

TMG—Tactical missile group.

TMP—Temperature.

TMPRLY—Temporarily.

TMPRY—Temporary.

TMS—Temperature Measurement Society.

TMTC—Tri-mode tape converter (tape-to-tape converter developed by Daystrom).

TMW—Tactical missile wing.

TNA—Tetranitroaniline (explosive). Time of nearest approach (satellite term).

TNC—Track Navigation Computer.

TNF—Transfer on no overflow.

TNL—Terminal net loss (telephone term).

TNM—Tetranitromethane (used in rockets).

TNT—Trinitrotoluene (explosive).

TNX—Thanks.

TNZ—Transfer on non-zero.

TO—Tandem outlet (telephone term). Technical Order.

TOC—Television Operating Center.

TOD—Technical **objectives** documents. Technical Operations Department. Time of day.

TOE—Total operating expense. Trainborne operational equipment.

TOF—Time of flight.

TONLAR—Tone-operated net loss adjuster receiving.

TOSBAC—Toshiba scientific and business automatic computer (developed by Tokyo Shibaura Electric Co., Ltd., Japan).

TOSS—Tiros operational satellite system. Transient or steady-state temperature (IBM-7090 code program).

TOT—Time on target.

TOW—Tube-launched optically-tracked wire-guided (anti-tank Army missile).

TP—Parallel tinsel cord (rubber). Telephone. Test point. Tie point. Tin plate. Top priority. Total pressure. Triple-pole.

TPA—Technical Publications Announcements (NASA — biweekly journal).

TPC—Time polarity control.

TPFW—Three-phase full-wave.

TPHW—Three-phase half-wave.

TPI—Trim position indicator. Turns per inch.

TPL—Median path loss during test period. Terminal per line. Transistorized portable laboratory. Turns per layer.

TPM—Tape preventive maintenance. Tri-plate module (developed by Sanders Associates, Inc.).

TPOM—Tube propagation d'ondes magnetron (crossed-field tube).

TPPD—Technical program planning document (U.S. Air Force).

TPR—Tape programmed raw (data scanner manufactured by Daystrom). Telescopic photographic recorder. Transmitter power rating.

TPRC—Thermophysical Properties Research Center (Purdue University).

TPS—Terminal per station.

TPT—Parallel tinsel cord (thermoplastic).

TQE—Technical quality evaluation.

TR—Carrier-test relay. Temperature recorder. Tetrode. Time-delay relay (JIC and NMTBA term). Time to retrofire. Tons registered. Transfer. Transfer reset. Transformation ratio. Transmit receiving. Transmitter. Trimmer. Tunnel rectifier.

TRA—Triaxial recording accelerometer.

TRAAC—Transit research and attitude control.

TRACALS—Traffic control, approach and landing system.

TRACE—Tape-controlled recording and automatic checkout equipment (developed by Blackburn Electronics, Ltd., England). Taxiing and routing of aircraft coordinating equipment. Tracking and communications, extraterrestrial. Transistor radio automatic circuit evaluator (developed by Philco).

TRADEX—Target resolution and discrimination experiments (a long-range tracking radar developed by RCA for Project Press).

TRADIC—Transistorized airborne digital computer (developed by Bell Labs for U.S. Air Force).

TRADIS—Tape repeating **[Cont.]**

automatic data integrating system.

TRASTA—Training Station (U.S. Navy).

TRC—Temperature-recording controller. Transmitter circuit (teletype abbreviation). Transportation Research Command (Ft. Eustis, Va.).

TRDET—Trouble detection.

TRDTO—Tracking radar takeoff.

TRE—Telecommunications Research Establishment (British laboratory). Timing read error.

TREAT—Transient reactor test facility (at Argonne National Laboratories).

TRECOM—Transport Research and Engineering Command (U. S. Army).

TRI—Technical Research Institute (Japan Defense Agency research group). Torsion reaction integrating.

TRIC—Tri-camera mount.

TRICE—Transistorized real time incremental computer, expandable (Packard-Bell digital computers).

TRIGA—Training research isotope (-production) general atomic reactor (built by DOFL and General Dynamics Corp.).

TRIM—Test rules for inventory management.

TRIPOLD—Transit injector Polaris-derived (developed by Lockheed).

TRIXIE—Transistors and Nixie tube (Sylvania-designed computer readout circuit).

TRL—Transistor-resistor logic.

TRM—Time ratio modulation.

TRML—Terminal.

TRN—Transfer.

TRODI—Touchdown rate-of-descent indicator.

TRP—TV remote pickup.

TRR—Teaching and research reactor.

TRS—Tetrahedral research satellite.

TRVM—Transistorized voltmeter.

TS—Carrier-test switch. Jacketed tinsel cord (rubber). Target strength. Tensile strength. Threaded studs. Timing selector. Tip speed. Tool sharpness. Transfer set.

TSAC—Title, subtitle, and caption.

TSADV—Television Service Association of the Delaware Valley.

TSAM—Television Service Association of Michigan.

TSC—Tactical support center. Transmitter start code. Transportable communications system.

TSCC—Telemetry Standards Coordination Committee.

TSD—Technical support directorate.

TSDAGR—Television Service Dealers' Association of Grand Rapids.

TSDI—Tactical situation display indicator.

TSEM—Transmission secondary emission multiplier.

TSG—Teflon (extruded), shield, silicone-impregnated fiber glass (cable term).

TSGA—Three-conductor, shipboard, general use, armored (cable term).

TSJ—Teflon (extruded), shield, and Teflon jacket (cable term).

TSK—Time-shift keying.

TSMT—Transmit.

TSO—Technical standard order. Test Support Office.

TSR—Transistor saturable reactor.

TSS—Tangential signal sensitivity. Technical specification sheet.

TST—Jacketed tinsel cord (thermoplastic).

TSW—Selector or transfer switch (NMTBA term). Transmitting slidewire.

TT—Teletypewriter. That. Thermostat switch (NMTBA term).

TTAT—Television technicians' Association of Tillamook (2108 8th

St., Tillamook, Ore.).

TTC—Tight-tape contact.

TT & C—Tracking, telemetry, and command.

TTCE—Tooth-to-tooth composite error.

TTHFWA—Twisted-pair, telephone, heat- and flame-resistant armored cable.

TTL—Transistor-transistor logic.

TTMS—Telephoto transmission measuring set.

TTPO—Twisted-pair, telephone, oil-resistant, portable, synthetic insulation, binder, impervious sheath cable.

TTR—Tape-reading tripping relay. Target track radar. Time-temperature recorder. Tonopah test range.

TTRC—Transistorized thyratron ring counter.

TTRS—Twisted-pair, telephone, radio, shielded, synthetic insulation, binder, impervious sheath cable.

TTRSA—Twisted-pair, telephone/radio, shielded and armored cable.

TTS—Teletypesetter.

TU—Task Unit. Tape unit. Thank you. Timing unit. Transmission unit.

TUG—Transac users' group.

TUN—Transfer unconditionally.

TUR—Traffic usage recorder (telephone term).

TV—Test vehicle (missiles). Traffic units. Traverse (JIC and NMTBA term).

TVA—Tennessee Valley Authority.

TvB—TV Bureau (TV service association, 1823 N. Michigan St., Elkhart, Ind.).

TVC—Temperature-control valve. Thrust vector control. Timed vital capacity (medical term).

TVI—Television interference.

TVIC—Television Interference Committee.

TVIG—Television and inertial guidance.

TVL—Tenth-value layer.

TVM—Tachometer voltmeter (JIC and NMTBA term). Transistorized voltmeter.

TVOR—Terminal VHF omnidirectional range.

TVSM—Time-varying signal measurement.

TVSO—Television space observatory.

TVTVA—Tualatin Valley Television Association (Aloha, Ore.).

TW—Moisture-resistant thermoplastic wire. Typewriter.

TWA—Traveling-wave amplifier.

TWG—Telemetry working group (division of the Inter-Range Instrumentation Group).

TWIS—Technical Writing Improvement Society (P.O. Box 5453, Pasadena, Calif.).

TWK—Traveling-wave klystron.

TWM—Traveling-wave maser.

TWOM—Traveling-wave optical maser.

TWPA—Traveling-wave parametric amplifier.

TWR—Control tower. Traveling-wave resonator.

TWS—Tail warning set. Track-while-scan.

TWSO—Tactical weapon systems operation (Aeronutronic division of Ford).

TWT—Traveling-wave tube.

TWX—Telegraph. Teletype. Bell system teletypewriter exchange service.

TX—Time to equipment reset.

TX-O—Transistorized experimental (Massachusetts Institute of Technology digital computer).

TYS—Tensile yield strength.

TZM—Titanium-zirconium-molybdenum alloy.

U

U—Underwater launched (Dept. of Defense missile designation). Unit. Unclassified. Up (JIC and NMT-BA term).

u—Micro. Unified (atomic mass unit).

U_a—Unit of activity (a term used in electroencephalography).

UACTE—Universal automatic control and test equipment (developed by Pacific Automation Products, Inc.).

UAL—Upper acceptance limit.

UAM—Underwater-to-air missile.

UAR—Upper atmosphere research.

UASCS—United States Army Signal Center and School (Ft. Monmouth, N. J.).

UBC—Universal buffer-controller.

UBSO—Uinta Basin Seismological Observatory (Vernal, Utah).

UC—Upper case.

UCA—Unitized component assembly.

UCC—Uniform commercial code.

UCCRS—Underwater coded command release system.

UCCS—Universal camera control system.

UCL—Unclamp (JIC) and NMT-BA term). Upper control limit.

UCPTE—Union for The Coordination of Production and Transmission of Electricity (European organization).

UCS—Universal connector strip.

UDC—Universal decimal classification.

UDMH—Unsymmetrical dimethyl hydrazine (missile fuel).

UDOFTT—Universal digital operational flight trainer, tool (developed by Sylvania for the U.S. Naval Training Device Center, Port Washington, N. Y.).

UDOP—Ultra-high-frequency doppler system.

UDT—Underwater demolition team. Universal data transcriber.

UDTI—Universal digital transducer indicator.

UDW—Ultra deep water.

UEC—United Engineering Center (between 47th and 48th Sts. at United Nations Plaza, New York, N. Y.).

UEL—Upper explosive limit.

UEP—Underwater electric potential.

UER—Unsatisfactory-equipment report.

UERMWA—United Electrical-Radio Machine Workers of America.

UET—United Engineering Trustees (owns and operates the United Engineering Center). Universal engineer tractor (U.S. Army crawler tractor).

UETA—Universal engineer tractor, armored.

UET(RT)—Universal engineer tractor (rubber-tired).

UEW—United Electrical Workers.

UF—Underground feeder.

UFCG—Underwater Fire Control Group.

UFCS—Underwater fire control system.

UFN—Until further notice.

UFO—Unidentified flying objects.

UG—Universal Government (coax connector).

UGGI—International Union of Geodesy and Geophysics).

UHF—Ultra-high frequency.

UHR—Ultra-high resistance. Ultra-high resolution.

UHS—Ultra-high speed.

UIO—Utility interative operation.

UJT—Unijunction transistor.

UKAEA—United Kingdom Atomic

Energy Authority.

UL—Ultra-linear. Underwriters Laboratories, Inc. (207 E. Ohio St., Chicago, Ill.). Upper limit.

ULF—Ultra-low frequency.

ULI—Universal logic implementer.

ULT—Uniform low-frequency technique.

ULTRACOM—Ultraviolet communications.

UMA—Ultrasonic Manufacturers' Association.

UMT—Universal military training.

UMW—Ultra-microwaves.

UNAECC—United Nations Atomic Energy Control Commission.

UNCOL—Universal computer-oriented language.

UNCOPOUS—United Nations committee on the peaceful uses of outer space.

UNE—Universal nonlinear element (developed by Comcor, Inc., Denver, Colo).

UNESCO—United Nations Educational, Scientific, and Cultural Organization.

UNICOM—Universal integrated communication system (U. S. Army global communication system).

UNIFET—Unipolar field effect transistor.

UNIPEDE—International Union of Producers and Distributors of Electric Power.

UNIPOL—Universal, procedure-oriented language.

UNM—Unified miniature (screw threads).

UNOPAR—Universal operator performance analyzer and recorder.

UNSC—United Nations Security Council.

UNSCC—United Nations Standards Coordinating Committee.

UNTRA—Union of National Radio and TV Organizations of Africa.

UOC—Ultimate operational capability.

UOV—Units of variance.

UPADI—Union Panamericana de Associaciones de Ingenieros (Federation of Pan-American Engineering Societies).

UPO—Unit Personnel Office (U. S. Army).

UPS—Uninterrupted power supply.

UPV—Unfired pressure vessel.

UPVC—Unplasticized polyvinyl chloride.

UR—Your.

URC—Utilities Research Commission.

URD—Underground residential distribution.

URLM—Upper reject limit for averages of acceptable lots.

URS—Universal regulating system. Yours.

URSI—Union Radio Scientifique International (International Scientific Radio Union).

US—Unconditional selection. Undersea. Uniform system.

USAADEA—United States Army Air Defense Engineering Agency (Ft. Meade, Md. Formerly U. S. Army Signal Air Defense Engineering Agency).

USAAFO—United States Army Avionics Field Office (St. Louis, Mo. Formerly U. S. Army Signal Avionics Field Office).

USAAMA—United States Army's Advent Management Agency.

USABAAR—United States Army Board for Aviation Accident Research.

USACE—United States Army Corps of Engineers.

USACWL—United States Army Chemical Warfare Laboratory (Edgewood Arsenal, Md.).

USAEB—United States Army Engineer Board.

USAEC—United States Atomic Energy Commission.

USAEMA—United States Army Electronics Materiel Agency (Philadelphia, Pa. — Formerly U. S. Army Signal Supply Agency).

USAEPG—United States Army Electronic Proving Ground (Ft. Huachuca, Ariz.).

USAERDA—United States Army Electronics Research and Development Activity, Fort Huachuca Ariz. (formerly U. S. Army Electronics Proving Ground, White Sands, N. Mex.; previously U. S. Army Signal Missile Support Agency). United States Electronics Research and Development Agency, Ft. Monmouth, N.J. (formerly U. S. Army Signal Research and Development Agency).

USAERDL—United States Army Engineering Research and Development Laboratory.

USAFAGOS—United States Air Force's Air-Ground Operations School (Keesler AFB, Biloxi, Miss.).

USAFE—United States Air Force, Europe.

USAFI—United States Armed Forces Institute.

USALMC—U. S. Army Logistic Management Center (Fort Lee, Va.).

USAMRDC—United States Army Medical Research and Development Command (Main Navy Building, Constitution Ave. and 18th St. N. W., Washington 25, D. C.).

USAOD—United States Army Ordnance District.

USAOGMS—United States Army Ordnance Guided Missile School (Redstone Arsenal, Huntsville, Ala.).

USAPC—United States Army Pictorial Center.

USAR—United States Army Reserve.

USARADCOM—U. S. Army Air Defense Command.

USAREUR—United States Army, Europe.

USARP—United States Antarctic Research Program.

USASC—United States Army Signal Corps.

USASSA—United States Army Signal Supply Agency.

USAT—United States Army Transport.

USATMC—United States Army Transportation Materiel Command.

USATRC—United States Army Transportation Research Command (Fort Eustis, Va.).

USB—Upper sideband.

USBBS—United States Bureau of Biological Survey.

USBEP—United States Bureau of Engraving and Printing.

USBF—United States Bureau of Fisheries.

USBGN—United States Bureau of Geographical Names.

USBIA—United States Bureau of Insular Affairs.

USBL—United States Bureau of Lighthouses.

USBLS—United States Bureau of Labor Statistics.

USBM—United States Bureau of Mines.

USBN—United States Bureau of Navigation.

USBNP—United States Bureau of Navy Personnel.

USBPR—United States Bureau of Public Roads.

USBR—United States Bureau of Reclamation.

USCC—United States Chamber of Commerce. United States Customs

Court.

USCG—United States Coast Guard.

USCGA—United States Coast Guard Academy.

USCGS—United States Coast and Geodetic Survey.

USCONARC—United States Continental Army Command.

USCSC—United States Civil Service Commission.

USDC—United States Department of Commerce.

USDD—United States Department of Defense.

USE—Underground service entrance cable.

USFS—United States Frequency Standard.

USGRR—United States Government Research Reports.

USGS—United States Geological Survey.

USHO—United States Hydrographic Office.

USIA—United States Information Agency.

USICIP—United States Committee for the International Conference on Information Processing.

USITA—United States Independent Telephone Association.

USL—Underwater sound lab.

USLA—Upper specification limit for averages of acceptable lots.

USM—Underwater - to - surface missile.

USMA—United States Maritime Administration. United States Military Academy. United States Military Attache.

USMAG—United States Military Advisory Group.

USMATS—United States Military Air Transport Service.

USMC—United States Marine Corps. United States Maritime Commission.

USMID—Ultrasensitive microwave

infrared detector.

USMM—United States Merchant Marine.

USN—United States Navy.

USNA—United States National Army. United States Naval Academy. United States Naval Aircraft.

USNAMTC—United States Naval Air Missile Test Center (Pt. Mugu, Calif.).

USNC—United States National Committee (International Electrotechnical Commission).

USNEDS—United States Navy Experimental Diving Station.

USNEL—United States Naval Electronics Laboratory (San Diego, Calif.).

USNG—United States National Guard.

USNMF—United States Naval Missile Facility.

USNMSC—United States Navy Medical Service Corps.

USNO—United States Naval Observatory.

USNPG—United States Naval Proving Ground.

USNPS—U. S. Navy Postgraduate School (Monterey, Calif.).

USNR—United States Naval Reserve.

USNRDL—United States Naval Radiological Defense Laboratory.

USNS—United States Naval Ship.

USNTDC—United States Naval Training Device Center (Port Washington, N. Y.).

USNUSL—United States Navy Underwater Sound Laboratory (New London, Conn.).

USNWC—United States Naval War College (Newport, R. I.).

USOM—United States Operations Mission.

USOMC—United States   **[Cont.]**

151

Ordnance Missile Command.

USP—United States Pharmacopeia.

USPHS—United States Public Health Service.

USS—United States Ship. United States Standard.

USSBS—United States Strategic Bomb Survey.

USSS—United States Secret Service. United States Steamship.

UST—Undersea Technology.

USW—Undersea Warfare.

USWB—United States Weather Bureau.

UT—Ultra - thin. Unipolar field - effect transistor. Universal time (new name for GMT—Greenwich Mean Time).

UTE—Union Technique de l'Electricite (French organization).

UTICI—Union Techniques des Ingenieurs Conseils (Paris, France).

UTL—Unit transmission loss.

UTP—Unit territory plan (Electronic Industries Association's plan for standardized rep - territory boundaries). Upper trip point.

UTR—University teaching reactor (developed by Advanced Technology Labs, Division of American-Standard). Unprogrammed transfer register. Up-time ratio.

UTS—Ultimate tensile strength. Unified transfer system (computer developed to translate Russian to English by Machine Translation Ltd., Washington, D. C.).

UTTC—Universal tape-to-tape converter.

UUA—Univac Users' Association.

UUT—Unit under test.

UV—Ultraviolet. Undervoltage (JIC and NMTBA term)

UVR—Ultraviolet rocket.

UV-VIS—Utraviolet-visible.

UWR—Under-weight rejector (developed by Illumitronic Systems Corp.).

UWS—Undersea weapon systems.

V

V—Control valve. Varnished cambric wire. Verbal. Video. Volt.

VA—Value. Value analysis. Vice admiral. Video amplifier. Volt-amperes.

V-A—Viper-Arrow (sounding rocket).

VAB—Vertical assembly building.

VAC—Vector analog computer. Video amplifier chain. Volts AC.

VAD—Voltmeter analog - to - digital converter.

VAFB—Vandenberg Air Force Base.

VAL—Variable-angle launcher.

VAM—Vogel's approximation method (mathematical programming term).

VANT—Vibration and noise tester.

VAP—VATE assembly program (developed by Mesa Scientific Corp., Inglewood, Calif.).

VAR—Variable. VHF visual-aural range.

VARACTOR—Variable reactor.

VASCA—Electronic Valve and Semiconductor Manufacturers' Association.

VAST—Versatile automatic specification tester (developed by Philco Corp.).

VATE—Versatile automatic test equipment (**Air Force project;** developed by Hughes Aircraft Co.).

VBI—Verein Beratender Ingenieure (German Association of Consulting Engineers).

VBWR—Vallechos boiling-water reactor (Pleasanton, Calif.).

VC—Vertical circle. Video correlator. Voltage comparator.

VCC—Visual Communications Congress.

VCG—Vehicle Control Group.

VCNO—Vice Chief of Naval Operations.

VCO—Voltage-controlled oscillator.

VCS—Vacuum - actuated control switch. Variable correlation synchronization.

VCSR—Voltage-controlled shift register.

VCXO—Voltage - controlled crystal oscillator.

VD—Vertical drive.

VDC—Volts DC. Voltage-to-digital converter.

VDCW—DC working volts.

VDE—Verband Deutscher Elektrotechniker (West German organization).

VDF—Very - high - frequency direction finding.

VDFG—Variable diode function generator.

VDI—Verein Deutscher Ingenieure (Society of German Engineers).

VDP—Vertical data processing (computer technique for multiple data processing developed by System Development Corp.).

VDPI—Vehicle direction and position indicator.

VDS—Variable depth sonar (developed by The Defense Research Board, Naval Research Establishment, Halifax, Canada).

VDW—Very deep water.

VE—Value Engineering.

VEDAR—Visible energy detection and ranging.

VERA—Vision electronic recording apparatus (video tape recorder developed by British Broadcasting

Corp.).

VERC—Vehicle effectiveness remaining converter (used in naval warfare simulator).

VERLORT—Very-long-range tracking radar (designed and built by Reeves Instrument Corp. for Discoverer ground-tracking program).

VESIAC—Vela Seismic Information Analysis Center.

VEV—Voice-excited vocoder.

VF—Fighter plane (U. S. Navy). Voice frequency.

VFB—Fighter bomber plane (U. S. Navy).

VFC—Voice-frequency carrier.

VFLA—Volume-folding and-limiting amplifier. ⋅

VFR—Visual flight rules.

VfR—Verein für Raumschiffahrt (Society for Space Travel—(German rocket society formed June 5, 1927).

VFT—Voice-frequency carrier telegraph terminal.

VGA—Variable-gain amplifier.

Vgh—Velocity, vertical acceleration, altitude.

VGSI—Visual glide slope indicator (developed by Sylvania).

VHB—Very heavy bombardment.

VHF—Very high frequency.

VHO—Very high output.

VHP—Very high performance. Very high pressure.

VI—Viscosity index.

VIAS—Voice interference analysis set.

VIB—Vertical integration building.

VIDAC—Visual information display and control (character-reproduction device developed by Columbia Broadcasting System).

VIDAT—Visual data acquisition, handling, storage, reduction, display, and recall system.

VIDIAC—Visual information display and control (devel- **[Cont.]**

oped by CBS Labs).

VIG—Video integrating group.

VIH—Velocity impact hardening.

VILP—Vector impedance locus plotter.

VINITI—Soviet All-Union Institute of Scientific and Technical Information (Moscow, USSR).

VINS—Velocity inertial navigation system.

VIP—Visual integrated presentation (Aircraft display).

VIPS—Voice interruption priority system.

VIS—Visual instrumentation subsystem.

VITA—Volunteers for International Technical Assistance.

VITROLAIN—Vitreous enamel porcelain.

VKF—Von Karman gas dynamic facility.

VL—Variolosser.

VLCR—Variable length cavity resonance.

VLF—Very low frequency.

VLFD—Via low frequency direct.

VLFS—Variable low-frequency standard.

VLN—Training glider (U. S. Navy).

VLR—Transport glider (U. S. Navy). Very long range.

VM—Vertical magnet.

VMC—Variable message cycle (telephone term). Visual meteorological conditions.

VMS—Vibration-measuring system.

VN—Training Squadron (U. S. Navy).

VNL—Via net loss (telephone term).

VO—Verbal orders.

VOA—Voice of America (Washington 25, D. C.).

VOCA—Voltmeter-calibrator.

VODACOM—Voice data communications.

VODER—Voice operation demonstrator.

VOL—Volume.

VOM—Volt-ohm-milliammeter.

VOR—VHF omnidirectional range.

VORDAC—Very - high - frequency omnidirectional range- and distance-measuring equipment.

VORTAC—Co-located VOR and TACAN Stations (VHF omnidirectional range and tactical air navigation).

VOS—Voice-operated switch.

VOX—Voice-operated control. Voice-operated relay.

VP—Valve positioner. Velocity pressure.

VPB—Patrol bomber (U. S. Navy).

VPC—Vapor fractometers. Voltage-to-pulse converter.

VPM—Volts per meter.

VR—Transport plane (U. S. Navy). Vendor rating (quality control term). Voltage regulator.

VRC—Viscometer recorder - controller. Visible record computer (developed by Burroughs).

VRF—Air Ferry Command (U. S. Navy).

VRPF—Voltage - regulating plate-filament.

VRPS—Voltage - regulated power supply.

VRSA—Voice - reporting signal assembly.

VS—Vacuum switch (JIC and NMTBA term). Video and sync.

VSB—Scout bomber (U. S. Navy). Vestigial-sideband.

VSC—Variable-speed optical chopper. Voltage-saturable capacitor.

VSCF—Variable-speed constant-frequency.

VSF—Vestigial sideband filter.

VSMF—Vendor-specs-micro-file.

V/STOL—Vertical/short takeoff and landing.

VSTR—Volt-second transfer ratio.

VSWR—Voltage standing-wave ratio.

VT—Utility plane (U. S. Navy). Variable thrust.

VTB—Torpedo bomber (U. S. Navy).

VTC—Vehicular traffic control.

VTO—Vertical takeoff.

VTOHL—Vertical takeoff, horizontal landing.

VTOL—Vertical takeoff and landing.

VTR—Video tape recorder.

VU—Volume unit.

V-V—Velocity-volume.

VVDS—Video verter decision stage (developed and manufactured by Epsco, Inc.).

VVR—Variable-voltage rectifier.

VWOA—Veteran Wireless Operators' Association.

VWP—Variable-width pulse.

Vx—Extinguishing voltage.

VY—Very.

W

W—Return loss. Watt. Waveguide. Weather (Air Force mission designation). Wire. Write. Writing.

WA—Waveform analyzer. Word add.

WAC—Women's Army Corps. Worked all continents. World Aeronautical Chart. Write address counter.

WACM—Western Association of Circuit Manufacturers.

WADC—Wright Air Development Center.,

WADD—Wright Air Development Division.

WADF—Western Air Defense Force.

WADS—Wide area data service.

WAF—Women in the Air Force.

WAFB—Wright-Patterson Air Force Base.

WALDO—Wichita automatic linear data output (computer programs developed by Boeing).

WAMOSCOPE—Wave - modulated oscilloscope.

WARM—Weapons assignment research model.

WAS—Worked all states (amateur-radio term).

WASCO—War Safety Council.

WASP—War Air Service Program.

Westinghouse Advanced Systems Planning Group. Wrapost aluminum systems panel.

WATA—Wisconsin automatic test apparatus.

WATS—Wide-area telephone service (telephone term).

WAVES—Women Accepted for Volunteer Emergency Service.

WB—Weather Bureau. Write buffer.

Wb—Weber.

WBAS—Weather Bureau Airport Station.

WBHO—Weather Bureau Hurricane Forecast Office.

WBNS—Water boiler neutron source (Atomics International).

WBO—Weather Bureau Office. Wide band overlapping.

WBR—Whole body radiation.

WC—Write and compute.

W/C—Wavechange.

WCATT—Worcester County Association of Television Technicians (Worcester, Mass.).

WCEMA—West Coast Electronic Manufacturers' Association.

WCF—White cathode follower.

WCM—Wired-core matrix memory.

WD—War Department.

WDD—Western Develop-   [Cont.]

ment Division (forerunner of Ballistic Missile Division).

WDGS—War Department General Staff.

WDMB—War Department Manpower Board.

WEDAC—Westinghouse Digital Airborne Computer.

WEDGE—Waterless electrical data generating effortless (spirometer).

WEMA—Western Electronic Manufacturers' Association (701 Welch Road, Palo Alto, Calif.).

WEPA—Welded Electronic Packaging Association.

WERS—War Emergency Radio Service.

WESCOM—Weapons system cost model.

WESCON—Western Electronic Show and Convention.

WESTAR—Waterways experiment station terrain analyzer radar.

WETAC—Westinghouse electronic tubeless analog computer.

WEW—Western Electronic Week.

WF—Write forward.

WFNA—White fuming nitric acid (missile fuel oxidizer).

WGL—Wissenschaftliche Gesellschaft für Luftschiffahrt (German Scientific Society for Aeronautics).

wh—Watt-hour.

WHIP—Wideband high - intercept - probability (receiver developed by Hallicrafters, Chicago, Ill.).

WHOI—Woods Hole Oceanographic Institution.

WI—Wrought iron.

WINA—Witton network analyzer.

WIP—Work in progress.

WITNESS—Wire installation tester for negating errors by sequencing and stationization.

WJCC—Western Joint Computer Conference (sponsored by IRE, AIEE, and ACM).

WL—Well. Will. Work light (NM-TBA term).

WM—Wattmeter (JIC and NMTBA term).

WMI—World Meteorological Intervals (IGY term).

WMO—Wing Maintenance Officer. World Meteorological Organization.

WMP—Weather - modification program (sponsored by National Science Foundation).

WMR—White Sands Missile Range.

WMSO—Wichita Mountains Seismological Observatory (Lawton, Okla.).

WO—Warrant Officer. Write out.

WOC—Without compensation.

WOG—Water, oil, gas.

WOJG—Warrant Officer Junior Grade.

WOO—Western Operations Office (NASA).

WORTAC—Westinghouse overall radar tester and calibrator (Canadian Westinghouse Co., Ltd.).

WOSAC—World wide synchronization of atomic clocks (U. S. Army Signal R & D Lab project).

WOTCU—Waveoff and transition control unit (Navy air traffic control system developed by Cornell Aeronautical Laboratory).

WP—Weatherproof.

WPC—World Power Conference.

wpc—Watts per candle.

WPL—Worst-month median path loss.

WPM—Mid-range wartime requirements plan (U. S. Air Force). Words per minute.

WPS—Short-range wartime requirements plan.

WPSL—Western Primary Standard Laboratory (Naval Industrial Reserve Ordnance Plant, Pomona, Calif.).

WR—Waveguide, rectangular.

WRAP—Weapon readiness achievement program (U.S. Navy maintainability system).

WREDAC—Weapons Research Establishment digital automatic computer (Elliott Bros.).

WRH—World Radio Handbook.

WRK—Work.

WRM—War readiness materiel.

WRS—Weather radar system.

WSAWD—White Sands Air Weather Detachment.

WSC—Western Simulation Council.

WSEC—Washington State Electronic Council.

WSED—Weapons Systems Evaluation Division.

WSEG—Weapons System Evaluation Group.

WSEM—Weapons System Evaluation Missile.

WSG—Winter Study Group (U. S. Air Force).

WSI—World synoptic interval.

WSMR—White Sands Missile Range.

WSPE—Washington Society of Professional Engineers.

WSPG—White Sands Proving Ground.

WSPO—Weapon System Project Offices (expedites the economical and timely delivery of a weapon system to an operational command).

WSSA—Write Sands Signal Agency.

WSSCA—White Sands Signal Corps Agency.

WSSL—Western Secondary Standards Laboratories (U. S. Navy).

WST—Weapon system, training.

WT—Bandwidth-duration product.

WTD—World Trade Directory (published by U. S. Dept. of Commerce).

WTR—Westinghouse Testing Reactor (Waltz Hill, Pa.).

WUX—Western Union telegram.

WVT—Water vapor transmission.

WVTR—Water vapor transmission rate.

WWM—Welded-wire matrix.

WWP—Working water pressure.

WX—Weather. Weather station.

X

X—No connection. Reactance. Reactor (JIC and NMTBA term). Research (Air Force Mission designation).

XB—Crossbar. Exploding bridge-wire.

XBT—Crossbar tandem (telephone term).

XEG—X-ray emission gauge (developed by General Electric X-ray Department).

XFA—Crossed-field acceleration.

XHV—Extreme high vacuum.

XLR—Experimental liquid rocket.

XLT—Lateral-telling.

XM—Experimental missile.

XMSN—Transmission.

XMT—Transmit.

XMTR—Transmitter.

XPD—Cross-polarization discrimination.

XRCD—X-ray crystal density.

XREP—Auxiliary report.

XS—Extra strong.

XSL—Experimental Space Laboratory.

XSPV—Experimental solid - propellant vehicle.

XTAL—Crystal.

XTM—Voltage-tunable magnetron.

XXS—Double extra strong.

XYL—Wife.

Y

YA—Ash lighter (U. S. Navy).
YAP—Yaw and pitch.
YC—Open lighter (U. S. Navy).
YCF—Car float (U. S. Navy).
YCTA—Yamhill Country Television Association (210 N. Evans St., McMinnville, Ore.).
YD—Floating derrick (U. S. Navy).
YEB—Yorkshire Electricity Board (British electrical power agency).
YIG—Yttrium iron garnet.

YL—Young lady.
YM—Prototype missile.
YMS—Motor minesweeper (U. S. Navy).
YN—Net tender (U. S. Navy). Yeoman (U. S. Navy).
YO—Harbor tanker (U. S. Navy).
YPD—Pile driver (U. S. Navy).
YR—Year.
YSP—Salvage pontoon (U. S. Navy).

Z

Z—Impedance.
ZA—Zero and add.
ZAR—Zeus acquisition radar (Nike-Zeus system).
ZD—Zone description.
ZE—Zero-effusion.
ZEBRA—Zero energy breeder reactor assembly.
ZED—Zero energy, heavy - water - moderated reactor.
ZEEP—Zero energy experimental pile.
ZEL—Zero length launch.
ZEPHYR—Zero energy fast reactor (Harwell, England).
ZETA—Zero energy thermonuclear apparatus (Harwell, England).
ZETR—Zero energy thermal reactor (Harwell, England).
ZF—Free balloon (U. S. Navy).
ZFB—Signals fading badly.
ZGS—Zero gradient proton synchrotron.
ZIP—Zinc-impurity photodetector.
ZIP CODE—Zoning improvement plan code (U. S. Post Office code for processing outgoing mail by electronic equipment).
ZK—Barrage balloon (U. S. Navy).
ZMAR—Zeus multifunction array radar (developed by Sylvania).
ZNN—Nonrigid training airship (U. S. Navy).
ZNP—Nonrigid patrol airship (U. S. Navy).
ZOE—Zero-energy.
ZPA—Zeus program analysis.
ZPR—Zero power reactor.
ZS—Zero and subtract. Zero suppress.
ZT—Zone time.
ZTO—Zone Transportation Officer (U. S. Army).